ABOUT THE AUTHOR

Dr. Dale was born and educated in New Zealand. He taught at Auckland School for Deaf children for four years

Enrolled at University of Manchester. His post graduate research study was in paedo-audiology. Supervisor Professor Sir Alexander Ewing, External examiner Professor Sir Frederick Bartlett, Department of Psychology, University of Cambridge. Awarded Ph.D degree - 1958.

After training teachers of deaf children for 3 years in Christchurch, Dr. Dale was appointed principal of the Auckland School for Deaf Children in New Zealand. In 1965 he was invited to apply for the post of Senior Lecturer in Audiology and Education of the Deaf at the University of London. Dr. Dale has since lectured widely in the United States and Canada, as well as in Europe, India and Pakistan, Ghana, Kenya and Uganda, Hong Kong, Mexico and Australasia.

He has published four books:-
- Applied Audiology for Children
- Deaf Children at Home and at School
- Language Development in Deaf Children
- Individualised Integration of Deaf Children

He was awarded an M.Sc. from the University of Cambridge in 1987 for his study of 'The psychological investigation of intellectual development in deaf children".

Awards:
1962	Principal, Auckland School for Deaf Children
	First president at New Zealand Residential Child Care Association
1963	Carnegie Travelling Scholar - USA and UK
1976	Alexander Graham Bell International Lecturer
1977	UK representative, UNESCO, Paris, International Conference on mainstreamed education
1984	Arranged Commonwealth Society for the Deaf lecture tour of India

Since 1970 Dr. Dale has been chairman or a principal speaker on the subject of mainstreaming deaf children and students into ordinary schools and colleges at five international conferences for teachers of the deaf.

Dr. Dale has two adult children in the United Kingdom and is also interested in music, gardening, art history, golf and rugby football.

FOREWORD TO FIRST EDITION

It gives me great pleasure to have an opportunity to recommend this book. As its title indicates it has been written as a source of immediate and practical help both to professional workers who have responsibility for all categories of hearing-impaired children and to parents. Its very great merit is the skill with which Dr. Dale has summarised and explained (for the most part in everyday language) results of modern research on hearing, speech and deafness by many workers, spot-lighting their relevance to the day-to-day needs and problems for children with varying degrees and types of deafness.

Treating in the same way the results of his own extensive experience as investigator and teacher, in New Zealand and in England, he has described tests of capacity to hear speech and to benefit from amplification for children of different ages; ways of ensuring that hearing aids are maintained in good order; methods of auditory training and the information that is needed by teachers in ordinary schools who have pupils with defective hearing in their classes.

Dr. Dale shows keen awareness of an urgent need to give deaf children as full experience of hearing as contemporary electronics make physically possible; widening its scope to make all possible sounds of daily life meaningful, even although many of the children can be enabled to hear them a good deal less completely than ordinary people. Some of his case histories are particularly valuable and relevant to this point. His own research, both in England and New Zealand, has taught him that parents and teachers and children themselves, need special training, knowledge and skill if the hearing aids are to be used to full advantage and throughout the children's waking hours.

The book includes numerous illustrations. A notable example is a series of photographs of visible speech recordings that show scientifically (in terms of spectrographic analyses) just how people can help hearing aid users by the manner of their phonation and articulation. There is an excellent index and bibliography.

I have come to believe in recent years that from the standpoint of education audiology is as yet too much based on work with deafened adults. Dr. Dale's book is one of the first to deal specifically with the audiological problems of children - at home and at school - who do not hear normally while they are growing up.

Professor Sir Alexander W.G. Ewing
The University,
Manchester, England

Third Edition

APPLIED AUD

FOR

CHILD

By

D.M.C. DALE B.A., (Auck.) M.Sc., (Cambridge.), Ph.D. (Manch.)

*(Formerly Senior Lecturer in Audiology and Education
of the Deaf, University of London,
Institute of Education, England)*

With Forewords by

Professor Marion P. Downs,
Department of Otolaryngology,
Health Sciences Center,
University of Colorado

and

The late Professor Sir Alexander W.G. Ewing
*The University of Manchester
Manchester, England*

JACKMUR PUBLICATIONS CYF
49 Linkside, London N12 7LE, England

Published and Distributed Throughout the World by

JACKMUR PUBLICATIONS CYF
49 Linkside, London N12 7LE, England

ISBN No. 0 9536193 0 3

First Edition, 1962
Second Edition, First printing, 1967
Second Edition, Fifth Printing, 1985
Third Edition, First printing, 2000

FOREWORD TO THE THIRD EDITION

With this third edition, *Applied Audiology for Children* becomes a classic. As valuable as the first editions were to parents and clinicians, this updated and state-of-the-art revision becomes even more useful to care-takers and professionals. Dr. Dale has drawn again on his immense experience to select those facets of technical audiology and auditory education that will be most useful and meaningful to parents, audiologists and deaf educators.

Dr. Dale is part of a distinguished English tradition of educators and scientists that we Americans recognize as being the forerunners of deaf education and audiological application. The Foreword to the first edition of this book represents one of the most notable of this group, Sir Alexander Ewing, who contributed so much to the advancement of oral education of the deaf. Dr. Dale continues that tradition under modern-day conditions.

One of the unique contributions of this book is that it describes the historical development of many present theories and procedures; among these are the origins of recruitment theory, speech reception testing, sound amplification, cochlear implants, immittance measures, etc. It is a pleasure to renew acquaintance with the pioneers who have been responsible for so much of our present knowledge. Dr. Dale shares my respect for these trailblazers.

Dr. Dale himself is still an innovator. He describes three new speech tests that can be used with very deaf children; and he continually expands his clinical techniques for presenting sound and for teaching speech to the deaf. He is indeed a master clinician who can transmit his effective teaching methods with great clarity. It is this clinical skill that makes the term "Applied" have meaning; for example, he shows how the research on temporal detection can be used to identify who will be the more intelligible speakers among the deaf.

Classroom teachers would benefit greatly from this book's description of how hearing aids should be cared for and used in the classroom. Along with parents, teachers in America as well as in England should read this book for a comprehensive background on how to manage the child with a hearing aid.

In this book Dr. Dale brings three things to the field: first, immense wisdom accumulated from many years of experience; second, technical knowledge that he constantly up-dates; and third, a firm viewpoint that he is not afraid to express on many points such as the auditory-oral approach, individualized methods of teaching, and even on the price of hearing aids. (He suggests that other countries take advantage of England's ability to produce good hearing aids at little cost, thus eliminating the enormous expense of hearing aids {such as in America!}). He will find much support for this idea.

It has been a delightful experience for me to read Dr. Dale's new edition, and I hope that parents, teachers, audiologists and otolaryngologists in both England and America will find it useful in their lives.

Marion P. Downs, M.A., D.H.S.
Professor Emerita,
Department of Otolaryngology
University of Colorado Health
Sciences Center
Denver, Colorado, U.S.A.

PREFACE TO THE FIRST EDITION

This book is written to help teachers, parents, audiologists, doctors, and other workers in audiology clinics make the most use of sound in the educational and social treatment of deafness.

There are numerous factors which seem to assist deaf children to overcome their communication difficulties. These might include: the tremendous contribution which well trained parents can make during the child's early years; the importance of well equipped schools, and able headmasters who are genuinely interested in deaf children; well trained teachers; the closest possible liaison between home and school; and regular association with normally hearing children who have been shown how best to help the deaf ones. The use of hearing aids should be viewed in relation to these other factors. For many children and adults an aid can enable them to carry on a virtually normal conversational life which would be quite impossible without it. For others, where the deafness is more severe, the effect of wearing a hearing aid is neither so noticeable nor so immediate. Further evidence is given in this book, however, of the benefit which hearing aids can be, even to children and adults who are profoundly deaf.

It is felt that if those who work in this field possess an elementary knowledge of the nature of sound, and of the means of amplifying it and presenting it to deaf children, they will be better able to ensure that the children receive the most intelligible, the most meaningful, and the most continuous experience of sound, that their residual capacity to hear permits.

Very grateful acknowledgement is made to the Medical Research Council for financial assistance given while conducting much of the research reported in this book. I wish to thank also Professor Sir Alexander Ewing and members of the staff of the Department of Audiology and Education of the Deaf at The University of Manchester, for their assistance at all times. Numerous principals of schools for the deaf in England, Holland, Australia, and New Zealand, together with their teachers and deaf children, have been very kind and helpful to me, and I am greatly indebted to them all for this. The late Dr. C.V. Hudgins, Clarke School for Deaf, Massachusetts, very kindly gave assistance with interpreting the sonograms. Father A. van Uden, Instituut voor Doven, St. Michiels Gestel, Holland is responsible for most of the information in the section on music for deaf children. Finally, Dr. B.B. Harold, Assistant Director, Commonwealth Acoustic Laboratories, Sydney, has given very freely of this time and information, and has made valuable criticisms of several sections of the text.

D.M.C. Dale, *Teachers' College, Christchurch, N.Z.*

PREFACE TO THE THIRD EDITION

While retaining most of the material of the earlier editions of this book, a great deal of very significant research has been added and illustrations have increased from 20 to 66.

As previously, work that is particularly relevant to parents, teachers, audiologists and residential child care staff, has been given special emphasis. The above information is also relevant, of course, to teachers' aides; to speech therapists, teachers in ordinary schools (who are increasingly being asked to teach hearing impaired children); to nurses and to medical students in training.

Three particularly significant developments which have occurred in paedo-audiology recently have been: frequency modulated (F/M) transmission of sound; immitance measurements, and cochlear implants for children. Progress in these three fields has been discussed in Chapters 1, 3 and 11.

Techniques for taking accurate ear impressions and then making ear moulds which fit snugly and eliminate acoustic feedback has been considered in Chapter 9. The excellent work of D.B. Fifield and his colleagues in the National Audiology Centre in Sydney, Australia has been quoted in detail.

Professor Sir Alexander Ewing continually emphasised that every child should receive the most intelligible pattern of sound that his/her residual capacity to hear permitted. The section on speech tests of hearing in this text has been extended to include 3 new tests involving discriminations between words containing long and short vowel sounds. The fitting of the best hearing aids and devising the most appropriate audiological programmes for these children, can now achieve a degree of accuracy not previously possible for children so profoundly deaf.

The *listening reading speaking method (LRS),* has been re-emphasised in Chapter 10 and everyone dealing with hearing impaired children either individually or in groups, is urged to consider using it for parts of each day. Teachers in ordinary (regular) schools and colleges where one or more hearing aided children are enrolled, could gain insights into ways of managing these children by reading much of this book and particularly Chapter 10. LRS methods have proved useful also to teachers and parents of slow learners and other language disordered children.

As indicated earlier, some of the most sophisticated (and expensive) instruments and techniques available in the field of paedo-audiology are described. The World Health Organization (WHO) in 1995, however, suggested that over 1/3 of the world's population were so poor that they could not even afford to provide enough food for themselves. In consequence and providentially, tests of hearing are now available which cost very little indeed to obtain and to administer. These tests can be used very effectively in countries (and indeed parts of most countries) where more elegant tests and measures are not readily available.

It is felt that students of this subject should become acquainted with some of the pioneers in this field whose earlier researches have accounted for so much of our present day knowledge in audiology. Excellent earlier work of Watson and Tolan; Hudgins; Wedenberg; von Bekesy; the Ewings; Zwizlocki; Davis and Silverman; Dix, Hallpike and Hood; J.E.J. John; Raymond Carhart; van Uden; B.B. Harold and Ira Hirsh has all been retained and it has been a pleasure to do so.

In line with modern text-book publishing policy, references have been used rather sparingly. In consequence, valuable research findings have had to be included without full acknowledgement to the original authors. Opportunity is taken here sincerely to acknowledge this information. Students who wish to study any topics in greater depth might refer to their libraries' databases.

Screening tests of hearing for preschool and school-aged children are now described in Chapter 12. It is also strongly recommended - (Appendix 1:1), that the audiological, educational, social and financial advantages of *very carefully initiated and monitored* individualised mainstream programmes in the schools should be offered to all deaf children whenever possible.

Finally, and at the risk of straying from the strictly audiological field, it is recognised that not every deaf person is able, or wishes only, to mix socially with normally, hearing people. In consequence, it is believed that every city and large town should have good centres for those adult deaf people who so desire, to meet socially during weekdays and at weekends.

D.M.C. Dale
Linkside, London N12 7LE
England

APPLIED AUDIOLOGY FOR CHILDREN

CONTENTS

Chapter 1

SOUND AMPLIFICATION

THE NATURE OF SOUND

Sound is produced when there are rapid changes in air pressure. It thus originates in matter that is *vibrating*. Common vibrating objects are strings, reeds and membranes. When a tuning fork is struck, the prongs vibrate until they finally come to rest again. If the movement of one prong is examined it may be seen that it travels backwards and forwards as in Fig. 1:1. As the prong moves out, it pushes the air molecules in front of it into a little group. This is known as a *compression*. When the prong moves back and past its original position it creates a kind of vacuum behind it and this is called a *rarefaction*. As the prong moves outwards again, another compression results, and as long as it vibrates, compressions and rarefactions occur in the air.

Fig. 1:1

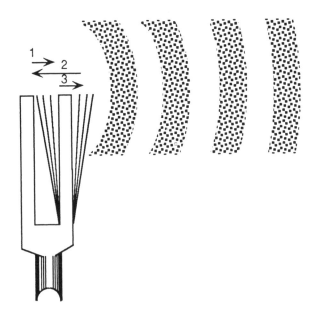

When the pulsations of air reach the ear, they are perceived as sound. If they come very rapidly, the sound heard is a high pitched one. If the pulsations come less frequently the sound is said to be low in *pitch*. Each time the prong of the fork (or the string of the violin, etc.) vibrates back and forth and back again to its original position (Fig 1.1 Movements 1, 2 and 3, it is said to have completed one *cycle*. A more accurate method of describing sounds than simply saying they are high or low pitched, is to measure the number of cycles occurring in the vibrating object every second and to express the number in terms of *frequency* (frequency being the number of cycles per second). Pitch is a subjective quality and does not imply numerical value, whereas frequency is an objective physical measure. When middle C on the piano is played, for example, the appropriate string moves back and right forward and then back again to its original position 256 times in every second. Middle C is therefore said to be a sound of 256 cycles per second (c.p.s.). The human ear is capable of perceiving sounds from as low as 20 c.p.s. to as high as 20,000 c.p.s. As will be emphasised later, however, the limited range in which the important components of speech sounds occur, lies between 300 and 3,000 c.p.s. (See Fig, 1:2 (a) below).

Fig. 1:2

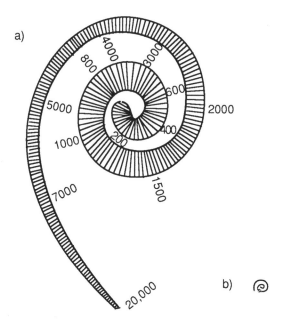

One further small complication occurred for students of audiology in 1968, when it was decided that the eminent German physicist, Henrick Hertz (1857-1894), should rightly be recognised for his pioneer work in this field.
Cycles per second were renamed *Hertz* and this was abbreviated to Hz. This symbol is now used internationally to denote cycles per second.

ELECTRICAL AMPLIFICATION OF SOUND

The principle involved in making sounds louder is the same in nearly all electrical amplifying systems whether they be public address systems at fair grounds, in theatres or railway stations, or the type employed in most varieties of hearing aids. Such amplifying systems usually contain three parts: (a) a *microphone*; (b) an *amplifier*; and (c) a *receiver* or *speaker* (Fig 1:3).

Fig. 1:3

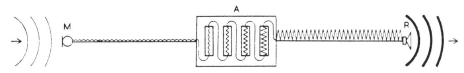

Sound travels through the air. As the sound wave impinges on the microphone, the pressure variations are transformed into voltage signals that are passed through the amplifier. The amplifier contains *tubes (valves)* or in the modern individual hearing aid, *transistors* or *integrated circuits*. The function of the amplifier is to make electrical waves larger, i.e., it amplifies the wave. The function of the receiver is to convert this enlarged electrical wave back into sound pressure - it is like a microphone working in reverse. Because the wave is much larger than the original, the sound produced by the receiver is louder than the sound that impinged upon the microphone. This, of course, is what the crowd or the audience or the deaf patient requires.

It is relatively easy to identify these three components in many of the hearing aids being used (Figs 1:4 and 1:16).

Fig. 1:4

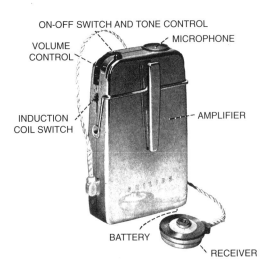

ON-OFF SWITCH AND TONE CONTROL
MICROPHONE
VOLUME CONTROL
INDUCTION COIL SWITCH
AMPLIFIER
BATTERY
RECEIVER

INPUT, GAIN AND OUTPUT

Input

The optimum input to a hearing aid microphone is about 70 dB* above SPL (speech perception level). That is about the level of conversational speech at a distance of three feet. A common fault of teachers and parents is that they speak much too loudly into the hearing aid. With 70 dB (or greater) input, and full volume control the output stage is likely to *overload*. Such overloading causes distortion of the speech and frequently a *reduction* in intelligibility rather than the desired increase.

In poor acoustic conditions it is wise to keep the voice at a reasonably high level, however, to achieve a good *signal to noise* ratio: i.e., plenty of voice entering the microphone excludes or at least helps to *mask out* the quieter background noises.

It is possible, by practising with a *sound level meter*, (See Fig. 2.9), to maintain the desired level of input to the microphone. In concentrating on keeping the correct level, however, one must be careful not to allow one's voice to become flat and uninteresting. Radio and television announcers usually have excellently controlled and modulated voices.

One should not be too concerned if occasionally the voice is raised above the best level. If, for example, a story is being told in which one of the characters is required to shout, then by all means let him/her shout. The word or words shouted may be distorted, but the story will not be spoilt by an unnatural presentation. One would have to consider abandoning the use of hearing aids if they unduly inhibited the teacher's style in the presentation of lessons.

Using the correct input level most of the time is just one of the many ways of ensuring that the children hear the clearest possible pattern of speech.

Gain

Hearing aids do not make all sounds equally loud, e.g., there is usually more emphasis given to the sounds between 750 and 3,000 Hz than to the frequencies above or below this range (Fig 1:5). Many hearing aids *peak* (have their maximum amplification) at 1,000 or 1,500 Hz. Because of this, and because 1,000 Hz is regarded as near the middle of the speech frequency range, the *gain* of a hearing aid is usually referred to as the amplification it gives at 1,000 Hz when switched to maximum.

Varying the response of a hearing aid can be achieved by adjusting the tone control on the aid or by using different receivers. The six lines at the left side of

---

* See End Notes p.26

Figure 1:5 are illustrations of different responses obtainable by manipulating the tone control of an individual wearable hearing aid.

Fig. 1:5

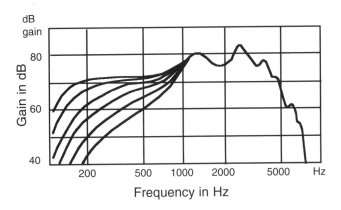

Output

The level of sound which comes from a hearing aid receiver is known as the *output* of the hearing aid. It may be calculated by the simple formula:

$$\text{Input} + \text{Gain} = \text{Output}$$

Thus if 60dB of sound enters the microphone, and the aid amplifies this by 45 dB, then the output of the aid is 105 dB (60 dB + 45 dB = 105 dB).

The majority of the better makes of individual hearing aids have a maximum output of 125 dB above 20 µPa*. (Previously .0002 dynes per square cm.) this output is quite adequate for the majority of hearing aid users but for the profoundly and subtotally deaf children it is often necessary to need greater output. This is frequently though not necessarily always achieved by increasing the battery tension. Makers of hearing aids usually state that if a 1.5 volt battery gives a maximum output of 125 dB, 3 volts will give a maximum output of 130 dB and 4 volts a maximum output of 135 dB above 20 µPa.

Simply increasing the amplification, however, is not always what is required. Often, for profoundly deaf children, it is most desirable to give the lower frequencies of the hearing aids more response, i.e., in the regions where a remnant of hearing remains, rather than just to increase the overall output.

It will be shown later that a knowledge of the output of hearing aids is very important to all audiologists, parents and teachers of the deaf and speech therapists, and is particularly so for those who deal with young deaf children.

---

* See End Notes p.26

RESPONSE CURVES

It is possible to measure the amount of amplification given by a hearing aid at different frequencies and to plot these measurements on a graph. Such data (Fig 1:5) are known as the *response curve* or the *frequency characteristics* of a hearing aid.

The production of audiometers in the early 1930's made it possible to measure with accuracy, a person's threshold of audibility for pure tones throughout a wide range of frequencies. Quite soon after this, the plausible hypothesis was advanced that if one could compensate in amplification the patient's hearing loss at each frequency, then near normal hearing should result. This practice was known as *selective amplification* or *audiogram fitting*, and seems to have received favourable consideration from nearly all audiologists during the 1930's and early 1940's. Towards the end of World War II, however, a large-scale research was initiated in the Electro-Acoustic Laboratories at Harvard University into the requirements of hearing aids. Evidence was produced regarding optimum frequency characteristics of hearing aids "... quite at variance with current thought and practice at the Aural Rehabilitation Hospitals, and with the preconceived ideas of the writers themselves."[41] The principles of selective amplification were shown *not* to represent the best response curves for hearing aids. A uniform frequency characteristic that could be varied by a tone control between a flat and a moderate accentuation of the high tones, proved to be the most satisfactory response for all or nearly all cases of hearing loss. Thus for the usual hard of hearing patient any detailed "fitting" of hearing aids was, the report said, "wasteful of time and effort". For the unusual and difficult cases, more elaborate selective tests were considered appropriate. Carhart in 1966 described a battery of these tests that he used in the selection of: (a) the best hearing aid from several instruments, and (b) the aid most suitable for the patient. These involved a consideration of certain dimensions of hearing aid performance - sensitivity or gain, signal to noise ratio, and efficiency in discriminating small sound differences. It was presupposed that patients possessed an adequate language background before such tests were attempted.

The Committee on Electro-Acoustics of the Medical Research Council of Great Britain published the results of an investigation similar to the Harvard study in 1947[101]. Experiments designed to determine the characteristics of a hearing aid suitable for general use were carried out during 1945 with sixty-three adult patients in the Otological Research Unit at the National Hospital, London. The results indicated: (a) that a cut off above 4,000 Hz was not detrimental to intelligibility, and (b) like the Harvard Report, that in order to achieve the best results the amplification between 750 and 4,000 Hz should be uniform or should increase with frequency.

LIMITING THE OUTPUT OF HEARING AIDS

The earliest hearing aids tended to boost both loud and soft sounds by the same amount. If, for example, a sound of 30 dB was presented to these aids, it might be amplified by 50 dB (to 80 dB). A sound of 70 dB would also be amplified by the same amount, so that the output would then be 120 dB. Apart from the fact that such loud sounds could be most unpleasant for the wearer, there was also a detrimental effect on intelligibility. It was realised that a better form of *limiting* should be incorporated in hearing aids.

Just after World War II, it was shown that if a communication system had insufficient amplitude handling capacity to pass the peaks of speech, but at the same time provided an adequate intensity level, maximum intelligibility could still be obtained by clipping off the peaks and using the available power for the remainder of the wave. The same principle was applied to radio transmitters and to hearing aids and it was shown that although 24 dB of peak clipping did affect the quality of the speech reproduced, there was no detrimental effect on speech intelligibility. In hearing aids, of course, the amplitude handling capability of the system is limited by the listeners threshold of discomfort. By introducing peak clipping it was now possible for hearing aid users to perceive the quieter sounds of speech undistorted and at louder levels than ever before and therefore attain greater intelligibility than was possible in aids containing undistorted amplifying systems.

Two years later, Hudgins and others[78] reported the results of a further investigation at Harvard. The comparative performance of four hearing aids was studied. Two were commercial aids without limiting, one was an experimental wearable hearing aid designed in the Electro-Acoustic Laboratory and including a compression type of automatic volume control, and the fourth was a Master Hearing Aid with variable characteristics. The experimental aid proved superior to the commercial aids particularly when the input signal was in excess of 70 dB. This research re-emphasized both the feasibility and desirability of using some form of limitation in individual hearing aids such as peak clipping or a compression type of *automatic volume control* (AVC).

With compression amplification, the wave is *gradually* reduced at the top (i.e., the loudest sounds), as distinct from the sharp cut off used in peak clipping (Fig. 1:6). The effect of such gradual limitation is alleged to give a more natural sound to the amplified speech than does peak clipping. As far as intelligibility is concerned, there does not appear to be a great deal of difference between the two types of limiting.

Fig. 1:6

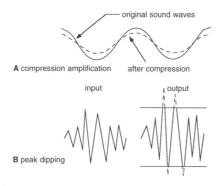

In a useful paper in 1993, Hawkins and Naidoo,[68] instead of considering statistically significant differences between word list or nonsense syllable scores, employed a *quality judgement* approach where subjects were asked to indicate which system of amplification they preferred: Listening to speech and music in good and poor acoustic conditions while amplifying systems alternated between peak clipping and compression amplification. A preference was found for compression amplification. This applied to both the quality and the clarity of the material heard. In addition, the preference became stronger with increases in the saturation of sound used. (It should be remembered that the 12 subjects in this experiment had only "mild to moderate" hearing losses. For profoundly deaf children, it is possible that peak clipping might still hold its own against compression amplification. Some audiologists, however, felt so strongly about this subject that they suggested that since over 80 percent of the 1.6 million hearing aids used in the United States were fitted only with peak clipping limitation, hearing aid manufacturers should consider compression type amplification to aids in the future).

James Jerger, too, noted in his editorial of the JAAA (April 1995), that the writers mentioning that peak clipping was detrimental to the harmonics of musical appreciation, was not exactly new. "Hallowell Davis and colleagues" he said "had pointed this out in the Harvard studies 45 years earlier."[41] He did emphasize, however, that in the more sophisticated approach of Hawkins and Naidoo, "the deleterious (harmful) effects of peak clipping" were more evident. Jerger hoped that these data would "send a strong message to hearing aid engineers and manufacturers".

Moore et al (1999) at Cambridge University and others, have shown that response curves can be very considerably modified to assist patients who have a reduced dynamic range (i.e. their threshold of detectability is very close to their threshold of discomfort, eg. Cases H and I on page 69).

Reference Levels

Physicists, when they design sound producing apparatus, use as their reference level an extremely slight sound pressure equivalent to 20 μPa. This point was first selected because it was the quietest level of a 1,000 Hz tone that could be heard in the free field by highly trained listeners.

To be audible to untrained listeners with average hearing, who are using earphones, it has been found that sounds need to be boosted by about 10 dB above 20 μPa at 1,000 Hz. At 250 Hz the tone must be increased by about 28 dB before it can be heard, whilst a really low-pitched sound, like 125 Hz requires nearly 50 dB above 20 μPa to make it audible (Fig 1:7). The differences do, of course, vary with different earphones. In making an instrument to test human hearing at various frequencies, (the audiometer) manufacturers cannot therefore use a scale that begins at 20 μPa. They take the points where each tone, through earphones, becomes audible to the average human ear, and call it *clinical zero*, i.e., the beginning of their decibel scale. The clinical zeros have now been standardized through the International Standards Organization.[38] The ISO levels are similar to those that were previously used as the British and European Standard.

The ISO line on the graph in Fig. 1:7 is the *threshold of audibility*. It is this line that appears as the straight "0" line along the top of present day audiograms. It is often called the threshold of detectability and more recently, the speech perception level (SPL).

Two zeros are thus being used in audiology, one is that of 20 μPa and the other is the normal threshold of detectability. The former applies primarily to the outputs of hearing aids, the latter to audiometers*, and to audiograms. When relating outputs to audiogram data (as for example when setting the output of a speech training hearing aid), it is necessary to deduct 15 dB from the marked output. This correction ensures that one is then calculating on approximately

Fig. 1:7

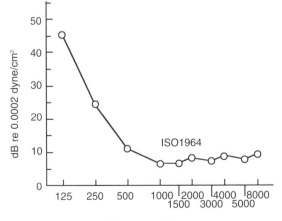

Frequency in C/S

_____

* Both pure tones and speech circuits

the same scale, since 15 dB is roughly the average difference between the two
levels throughout the speech range.

HEARING AIDS OF DIFFERENT TYPES

It is proposed here to discuss eight types of hearing aids in common use at the
present time: individual body worn hearing aids: behind the ear (BTE) aids; in
the ear (ITE) aids; completely in the canal (CIC) aids; frequency modulated
(FM) aids; infra red ray aids; group hearing aids and finally, speech training
(auditory training) aids.

Individual Wearable Hearing Aids

The ultimate development of this type of hearing aid has been one which fits
completely inside the ear canal and, for those people who benefit from *binaural
listening*, one can be worn in each ear. Manufacturers have produced aids of this
type but they have not so far proved very successful for severely deaf wearers.
Two difficulties with them are: (a) to obtain an effective seal around the mould
which will prevent *acoustic feedback* (leakage of sound from the receiver to the
microphone) - the receiver and microphone are of necessity placed within less
than 2cm of one another in such small instruments, and (b) when using such
miniature components, to provide the most desirable frequency response at the
receiver.

More success has been achieved with the slightly larger hearing aids worn
behind the ear (Fig. 1:8) or concealed in spectacles (Fig. 1:9), brooches, ear-
rings, hairclips, etc. These aids however, can be expensive to buy and to
maintain and service, and with little children, can be easily lost.

Fig. 1:8

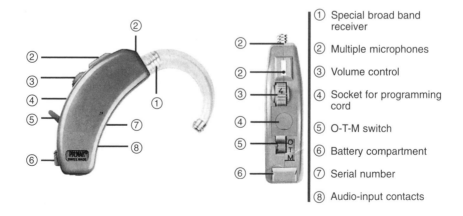

① Special broad band
   receiver

② Multiple microphones

③ Volume control

④ Socket for programming
   cord

⑤ O-T-M switch

⑥ Battery compartment

⑦ Serial number

⑧ Audio-input contacts

Fig. 1:9

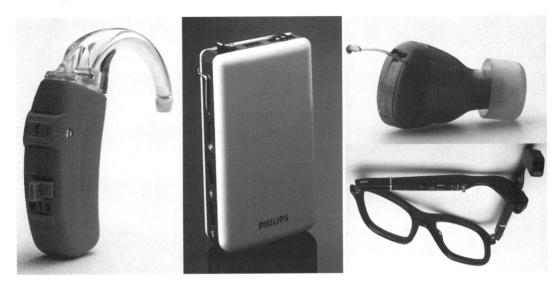

Behind the Ear (BTE) Hearing Aids

These little hearing aids (See Figs. 1:8 and 1:9) have been found particularly useful for most children - provided they have been taught to take care of them. Better ear impressioning techniques have enabled high levels of output to be used without the continual interference caused by acoustic feedback (See Chapter 9) when microphones are placed so close to receivers of aids. This, of course, is the case when ear level aids are used and high levels of gain are required. Wider frequency responses in ear level aids were possible after the new plastic materials (especially Teflon), enabled electret microphones to be housed in them (Coles-1987).[32]

Fig. 1:10

In Fig 1:10 Miss America of 1995 shows her BTE aid to one of the present "students" at John Tracy Correspondence Course Headquarters in Los Angeles.

Due to advances in the development of behind the ear hearing aids and ear impressions and in ear-mould making, bodyworn aids are rarely worn by children today. Experienced audiologists, however, warn against forsaking body-worn hearing aids prematurely in favour of the less obvious ear-level instruments.

Great care of course, should be taken to ensure that these large aids can be worn as comfortably and inconspicuously as possible (See Chapter 10).

When governments such as Great Britain or India set up a state hearing aid programme, it is found to cost only a fraction of that charged by commercial firms for similar instruments. (In Great Britain in 1996, government ear level hearing aids, for example, were able to be sold abroad for approximately £8 each - $12US. Sometimes similar commercial aids would sell for $120 - $130US).

It is suggested that in countries where the cost of hearing aids and servicing is almost crippling an auditory programme, parents and teachers might enquire through their Departments of Health and Social Welfare whether some other government such as Great Britain, India, or Australia might be able to assist with a bulk purchase of their inexpensive but highly satisfactory individual hearing aids for children.

As indicated in Chapters 9 and 10, those dealing with young children should expect far more breakages and stoppages than those catering for older children. Again, recent figures from London schools have shown that children from 0-5 years of age, for example, require their earmoulds to be replaced or enlarged 4 times each school year due to the rapid growth of their ears during these years. As the ear enlarges, of course, the earmould becomes loose and sound is able to escape in the gap left between the ear mould and the pinna. This whistling sound is called acoustic feedback and it can bedevil many infant programmes

Fig. 1:11

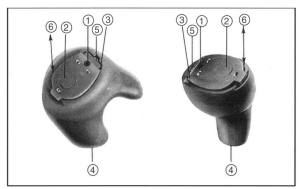

① Subminiature electret microphone

② Socket for programming cord

③ Snap-in/Snap-out electronic module

④ Receiver: different models to be selected according to ear size/degree of loss

⑤ Serial number

⑥ On/off switch integrated in battery compartment

(See Chapter 9). Children from 5 to 15 years of age, however, only require 2 or 3 changes of earmould annually and after that, only once per year.

Ear level hearing aids have been found to have far fewer breakdowns than body-worn aids. It is emphasised, however, that *all* hearing aids are sensitive instruments and need genuine care and attention if they can be expected to perform at maximum.

In an all-age school for severely deaf children in London in 1994, all of the children had been issued 2 ear level hearing aids. Apart from the daily checking of each child's hearing aid's performance, it was found that there was an average of just over one major breakdown requiring attention at the hearing aid clinic for every aid each school year.

Fig 1:12

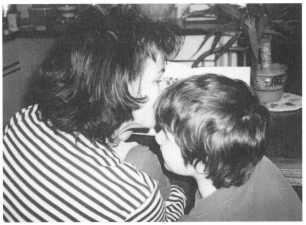

Two mothers enjoy listening and reading games with their children

Completely in the Canal (CIC) Hearing Aids

As briefly mentioned above, for less deaf children i.e., those whose average loss does not exceed 75 dB, completely in the canal (CIC) hearing aids are now available. These represent a major improvement in the miniaturisation of hearing aids and a commendable achievement in oto-acoustic design (See Figs. 1:13 and 1:14).

When microphones and receivers of a hearing aid are placed only 1-1.5cm apart, however, acoustic feedback restricts the amount of gain which can be incorporated in them. The cost of these hearing aid prohibits their being considered for most children at the present time and their low output renders them inadequate for approximately 70 percent of children who require to use hearing aids. It is believed, however, to be only a matter of time before the above problems are overcome.

To enable such tiny instruments to be removed each day, a 1cm plastic lead and bead has been attached (See Figs. 1:13 and 1:14).

Fig. 1:13

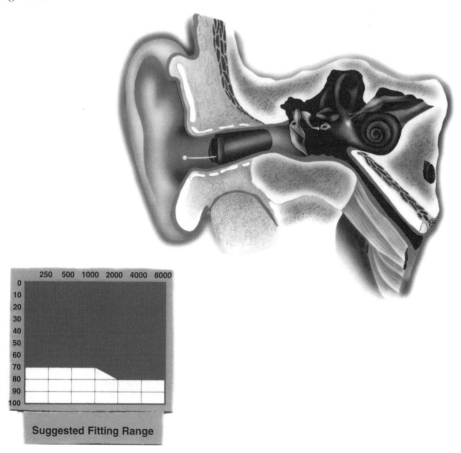

Suggested Fitting Range

Caution: CIC hearing aids should be considered only for children who are old enough to appreciate the cost and delicacy of such instruments. For younger partially hearing children, the behind the ear (BTE) hearing aids are still the most widely recommended.

Fig. 1:14

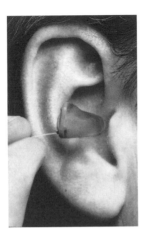

Frequency Modulated (FM) Hearing Aids

Frequency Modulated (FM) hearing aids are the modern equivalent of group hearing aids. With FM aids, the teacher wears a transmitter unit and each child wears a frequency modulated hearing aid. This enables both teacher and children greater freedom of movement (See Fig. 1:15).

Fig. 1:15

One disadvantage with FM aids, however, can be that a child may not hear his/her own voice properly, nor that of the other members of the class. Many FM aids *do* have microphones incorporated in them, of course, but in noisy class-rooms, (particularly with young children), extraneous noise can often interfere with intelligible speech reception. As is suggested later in this book, teachers (and parents) should always be prepared to 'have a listen' to a child's hearing aid to ensure that he/she is receiving the best possible listening experience. The writer recalls suggesting to a small child on a dreadfully noisy school bus into the city one afternoon that he might turn his hearing aid down until he was in more normal listening conditions, only to be informed quite frankly, "No, Me 5!" i.e. he had clearly been told earlier that position 5 would give him the best listening experience and he should be careful to keep his aid on that setting. An adult in such a situation, would, of course, have immediately turned his/her aid down, if not completely off, in such apalling conditions.

Group Hearing Aids

Group hearing aids seem first to have been designed in the late 1920's and early 1930's. Today, there is a variety of types of such aids. All are expensive. The advantages of group hearing aids are that, if properly used, they enable the children to hear loud sound in both ears with better high and low frequency response than is possible with insert receivers. Suggestions for using group hearing aids are included in Chapter 10.

Fig. 1:16 A group hearing aid

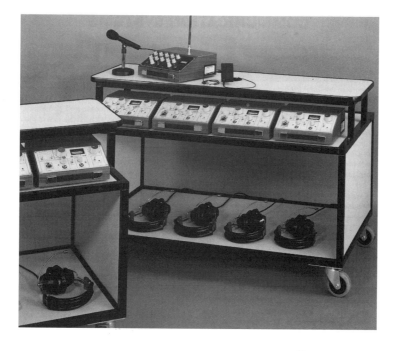

Modern group hearing aids as shown in Fig. 1:16 are much more flexible instruments than earlier. With the individualised units which make up these systems, teachers can use single, double or multiple units for group work. For older children, it is felt that such interconnected self contained auditory training devices can enable easy regrouping or splitting up of groups with a minimum of fuss. Inevitably, the use of radio microphones by teachers' has been a direct advantage in both special schools and classes and, of course, in individually mainstreamed situations.

If a radio collar or head microphone is used the teacher is enabled to speak close to it. Distance from the microphone does, of course, affect speech intelligibility, and where classrooms are noisy and reverberant, can be the deciding factor in whether aids are of benefit or not. (See Chapter 6).

Speech Training Hearing Aids (sometimes called Auditory Training Aids)
Speech training aids are table model, mains or battery operated individual aids (Fig. 1:17). One which was common in Commonwealth schools for the deaf is an aid that was manufactured by a commercial firm to specifications suggested by the Department of Audiology and Education of the Deaf at the University of Manchester. Such hearing aids have a frequency response which is more or less flat from 750 to 8,000 Hz with a monitoring switch for each ear marked in 5 dB steps up to a maximum output of 135 dB above 20 µPa. They also possess an input level meter, a gain control, and it is possible to connect a tape recorder or radio to them. (See Chapter 10). The input level meter and the gain control switch can both be particularly helpful when encouraging a child to use voice at

Fig. 1:17

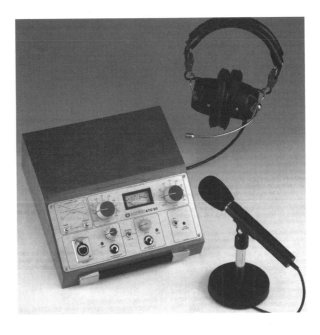

all and then to vary the loudness. At first, one uses a high gain position to show the child that by producing a sound, the volume needle will move. Later, by manipulating the control, one can help a child to appreciate loud and soft voice, how to sustain a sound for a period, thus gaining breath control which is required for producing sentences. Games can be played that are simple and useful in speaking later, e.g., say to the child "Can you do this?" and say "Ba baaa ba baaa". Follow this with other little rhythmical games "Mee Mor Mee Mor", etc. Sustained voice copying an elongated rhythmical "War war war" as the teacher lightly taps the top of his output meter and shows the child how many seconds the breath had lasted. All of these little games should be kept pleasant. The teacher remembering that as far as possible "All teaching should be fun". Little competitions with other children of similar ability can also help to maintain interest in these sessions, which should always be brief. Two or three children at a time can participate in a speech session.

Unfortunately, the cost of such instruments has prohibited their regular use by most children and, as with music practice, guidance and regular encouragement from interested adults is usually very necessary.

These high quality table model hearing aids are popular in most schools for deaf children and special classes for the hearing impaired. The speech training hearing aid illustrated in Fig. 1:17, is a rechargeable battery powered aid which has inputs for both student and teacher microphones. In special classes in regular schools, 2 such hearing aids can be coupled together and in schools for deaf children, 10 such aids can be connected together to provide a powerful group hearing aid for older children and students. Each earphone can be adjusted, of course, to the optimum listening level for each ear. Output is controlled in 5 dB steps.

At each ear an auxiliary input socket enables tape recordings and cassette or video taped material to be played or recorded for future use. One output will also drive a small induction coil (loop system) which is ideal for using with television and when the children are dancing.

The acoustic output of this type of speech training hearing aid is 135 dB above 20 µPa.

The makers claim that such aids have a virtually flat response from 100 Hz to 10,000 Hz. Bass and treble controls give a nominal 6 dB per octave cut or boost as required.

Another useful feature for teachers and speech therapists, is a meter that indicates exactly what level of sound is being delivered to each ear.

Many of the methods that we use in teaching speech are by no means new, and provide at best only an approximation of the true patterns or elements required. An instrument that has been designed for speech teaching, is one that can analyse short samples of speech as accurately as is done by the Sonagraph, (Fig. 5:6), but that is capable of making such analyses instantaneously and of retaining the display for several seconds, if necessary. By giving a child the correct pattern (either on another screen or on a chart), it is possible for him to practice until he has produced the same shape on his screen, i.e., he can monitor with his eye in the same way as the normally hearing child monitors with his/her ear.

The possibilities of such an instrument as that suggested above, seemed quite exciting. One could imagine, for example, that profoundly deaf infants could become interested in the visual patterns they could make on the screen with their voices, and could experiment much more purposefully.

Competent older children (and adults), after careful assessment of their abilities and imaginative regular encouragement, should find this an aid to obtaining and retaining intelligible speech at their particular level. One cannot work miracles, or course, and where a child's speech is non existent or really grossly defective or the access to a visible speech translator is infrequent or haphazard, success cannot be guaranteed or even expected. One wonders, however, what effect, say, 5 or 6 sessions each day might have on short samples of carefully chosen speech material when practised by a well motivated child who was also assisted by the best possible auditory equipment and visual aids and a competent, experienced, well liked and respected teacher on the child's speech intelligibility, especially if careful records were kept and shared with the child and his/her parents.*

Class teachers who do not have the assistance of aides or helpers find difficulty in making use of speech training aids. "How can we take one child for individual work and at the same time, keep the rest of the class *usefully* employed?" they ask. It is possible to do one session of individual work each week, but to try to get an hour or so every day is often extremely difficult. As a result of this, many of the speech training aids bought by schools are not used at all regularly.

If it is agreed that individual speech and auditory training work is valuable, there seem two possible means of providing it. One is by using a speech and auditory training specialist within the school who takes children from their classrooms for individual work. This method has the advantage that an experienced teacher is able to achieve much more in a given time than is an inexperienced one. There are some drawbacks, however. No matter how close the liaison between class teacher and specialist, the class teacher never really

---

* The writer was informed that Sir Yehudi Menuhin was still practising on the violin for 8 hours each day (only one year before he died).

seems to obtain the exact information about each child's speech and hearing abilities and disabilities that will be of most use to her when she is taking the class for the daily group speech lesson and at other times during the day. "Teaching the deaf to speak" is one of the most fascinating aspects of our work and one which many teachers, quite understandably, are reluctant to relinquish to someone else.

A second method, which involves one teacher being used in a peripatetic capacity, seems to have possibilities. One teacher, essentially an able, experienced and energetic one, goes to, say four classes for one hour each day and takes subjects decided upon by herself and the class teacher. Whilst she does this, the class teacher removes two (or three) children at a time to a quiet room nearby and takes individual speech improvement and auditory training work. On one occasion it was possible to run a similar scheme on an experimental basis, for a four week period.

When asked to comment at the end of the four week period, the three class teachers wrote:

1. "Even in the short and experimental period the scheme was in operation, the children's speech improved noticeably and for the first time a really satisfactory and accurate assessment of speech and hearing could be made."

2. "Once we'd got organised it was wonderful. Quite a few of the parents commented on the speech improvement ... The children themselves enjoyed the individual work. Afterwards they would ask why we were not still doing it ..."

3. "I'm quite certain that itinerant teachers can be of value and I'm looking forward to the time when we have another on our staff."

Such use of speech or voice training hearing aids may require additional staffing. If existing classes are not too large, however, it seems likely that by increasing the size of the classes a little, no increase in teaching staff should be necessary.

In "Individualised Integration" (See Appendix 1:1 and 1:2), data are presented which confirm the effectiveness of individualised methods of teaching over whole class or even small group methods. The purpose of this new approach is to assist hearing impaired and unhandicapped children to develop a close appreciation of each other's interests, abilities and difficulties but also to improve the deaf children's educational and auditory development. It can only be of advantage to the hearing impaired child who it is one day hoped will live happily in ordinary society, to receive a regular, daily input of the natural speech and language patterns of his/her classmates, teachers and welfare assistants.

The question of the advantages of *binaural listening*, has not yet been satisfactorily resolved. A number of writers have observed a lowering of the threshold of detectability of approximately 3 dB when either speech or pure tones are listened to first with one ear and then with both. In many cases, the ability to locate the source of sound improves when listening binaurally. There is also a growing body of evidence that many children (and adults) prefer to use two aids rather than just one. Neurologists state that the use of binaural aids seems reasonable to them. When word list tests of hearing are used, however, the differences in scores obtained when using monaural and binaural aids are seldom significantly different statistically. (One rather frustrated father commented to the writer that *he* favoured the use of two hearing aids, "Because" he said, "then at least *one* of them might be working!")

Today, two ear level hearing aids seem to be fitted routinely in all Western Countries as soon as an accurate assessment of a child's hearing threshold is obtained. Some audiologists will give parents a hearing aid for their child "to see how he likes it" but as is shown in Chapter 7, listening levels for young children need to be set with great care if each child is to be able to listen with optimum intelligibility and comfort.

Parents, after guidance from audiologists or advisory teachers of the deaf, are sometimes in the best situations to ascertain the optimum listening level and best frequency response for their little child. (See Fig. 1:12 and Chapter 7). In setting outputs of aids some children need assistance much longer than others, as is the case, of course, with all learning tasks.

Audio Zoom, (i.e., two directional microphones placed in some hearing aids) assist the wearers to focus in on the source of sound (rather like two telescopic lenses in cameras). The manufacturers claim that this enables wearers to exclude extraneous noise in a room as they concentrate on, for example, the voice of the person to whom they are talking. In other situations, when, for example, listening to an orchestra playing, they are able to switch to the *Wide Angle* position and hear all of the instruments at once.

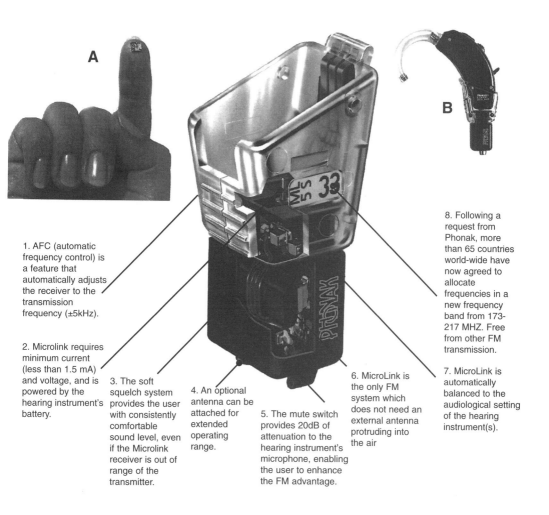

1. AFC (automatic frequency control) is a feature that automatically adjusts the receiver to the transmission frequency (±5kHz).

2. Microlink requires minimum current (less than 1.5 mA) and voltage, and is powered by the hearing instrument's battery.

3. The soft squelch system provides the user with consistently comfortable sound level, even if the Microlink receiver is out of range of the transmitter.

4. An optional antenna can be attached for extended operating range.

5. The mute switch provides 20dB of attenuation to the hearing instrument's microphone, enabling the user to enhance the FM advantage.

6. MicroLink is the only FM system which does not need an external antenna protruding into the air

7. MicroLink is automatically balanced to the audiological setting of the hearing instrument(s).

8. Following a request from Phonak, more than 65 countries world-wide have now agreed to allocate frequencies in a new frequency band from 173-217 MHZ. Free from other FM transmission.

Fig. 1:18 Uses of a hand held unit containing two microphones to aid directional listening in group and noisy classroom situations and also the FM transmitter.

Infra-red Rays in Remote Control Hearing Aids

Recent developments in audiological technology, involve the transmission of sound by infra-red rays (rather than electronically). The receiver and transmitter section is often worn on the chest of the speaker and is held in position by a neck cord which passes through an eyelet at the base of the receiver (See Fig. 1:15). The makers suggest when sound enters the microphone, it is immediately transmitted to the BTE hearing aid of the student (Fig. 1:19). Minimum interference occurs to the signal (voice of speaker or musical instrument, etc.) because infra-red rays are not affected by noise or reverberation.

The HandMic Unit
contains omnidirectional,
directional and super-
directional microphones, as
well s the FM transmitter in
one solid unit. It features
plug-in frequency modules for
transmission on any of the
frequencies reserved for use
by hearing impaired persons.
The HandyMic can be placed
either directly in front of the
sound source, slipped in the
speaker's shirt pocket, worn
on a cord around the neck, or
hand-held by the teacher and
aimed at the speaker. This
tool enables the teacher to
select the best sound quality
setting by switching between
the wide-angle, zoom and
super-zoom modes.

WIDE-ANGLE:
In group situations
the microphone unit
is placed in the
centre.

ZOOM:
By using 2 micro-phones
in tandem, speech signals
from the direction in which
the Handy Mic is aimed,
can be better received
than extraneous noice
from other directions.

SUPER-ZOOM:
In particularly noisy
conditions this setting
enables the microphone to
focus narrowly on one
speaker's voice which the
manufacturers claim
delivers "a crisp, clean
sound signal".

THE HANDMIC

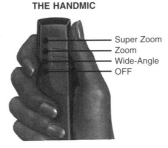

- Super Zoom
- Zoom
- Wide-Angle
- OFF

HANDMIC USED AS A
PASS-AROUND
MICROPHONE
in a group situation, such
as speech training where
all the students are
equipped with MicroLink or
MicroVox FM receivers, the
teacher may use the
HandyMic to pick-up the
speech of any student and
transmit it to the group.

Fig. 1:19 Uses of a hand held unit containing two microphones to aid directional listening in group and noisy classroom situations and also the FM transmitter.

The Induction Loop System

Most of the better makes of individual hearing aids today incorporate an induction coil for use with this system. Very roughly, induced sound for hearing aid wearers is used in the following manner. A microphone is coupled to an amplifier and from the amplifier a *loop* of wire runs around the room (Fig. 1:20). When the power is switched oh,, the current flow in the wire creates a magnetic field within the loop (and for some distance outside it). When a person speaks into the microphone, the sound wave is turned into a voltage signal and passes to the amplifier when it is boosted. This enlarged signal then runs into the loop of wire and is *transmitted* within the magnetic field, i.e., the electrical impulse has now become a radio wave. This radio wave is picked up or, more correctly, "induced into" the hearing aid by the induction coil (a tiny coil of copper wire). It is thus changed back to a voltage signal, and this eventually passes up to the receiver of the aid and is reconverted to a sound wave again. By using the induction system, the speaker is within a few inches of the microphone and the distance between him and the child is spanned with radio waves. Acoustic conditions are thus by-passed and the speech that is heard by this method in quite noisy and reverberant classrooms is clear and undistorted.

Although the child heard the teacher with beautiful clarity, it had not been possible for him to hear his own voice at all. This is such a serious limitation that the use of such a system in the normal classroom situation cannot be recommended. Hearing aids have been produced that are capable of being switched: (a) to the induction coil; (b) to the microphone of the aid, and (c) to a position where both the induction coil and the hearing aid were in action at the same time. When using this third position,, the child is supposed to hear the teacher's voice on the induction coil and his own voice via the microphone of his own aid. By switching in the sensitive little microphones of the individual hearing aids, however, one simultaneously switches in all the background noise

Fig. 1:20

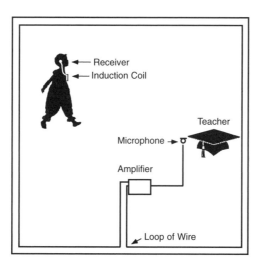

and acoustic disturbance which the loop system so successfully eliminates. In a normal, quite noisy little preschool (kindergarten) room, for example, it is not possible to determine any difference between the positions - microphone plus loop, and microphone only. To put it another way, interference picked up by the microphone masks out the clear speech that comes through the induction system.

Some contend that very good acoustic treatment of the rooms should eliminate much of the ambient noise which is being amplified, but this is often prohibitively expensive.

At last a form of "walkie-talkie" apparatus has been developed that enables two-way communication by radio waves from teacher to child (Fig. 1:20).

In ordinary school classrooms, at school assemblies, in ballet, eurhythmical work, etc., i.e., where mostly only one-way communication is required, induction loop systems have proved extremely effective. Teachers should ensure that the younger children have their aids switched on to the loop position at the beginning of each session, and switched on to the loop position at the beginning of each session, and switched back to normal listening at the conclusion. Small *transmitter microphones* have been produced for use with loudspeakers in theatres and with other public address systems. They seem to have distinct possibilities for hearing aid users in the school situations mentioned above. Teachers can wear the transmitter microphones and be free of the lead which normally connects them to the amplifer and induction loop. One objection to them at the moment is economic - both the purchase price and the running costs are at present too high.***

With the increased use of individualised mainstream programmes for most deaf children (See Appendix 1:1 and 1:2), group teaching and group hearing aids are, of course, becoming less common.

Loop systems can also be very useful when attached to television sets (and to radios provided, of course, the child is not too severely deaf). When using induction loops in this way, it is not necessary to purchase a microphone or amplifier. If it is desired to use the induction coil for *speech* in the home, then a microphone and an amplifier are necessary. It must be said, however, that the use of the system in this way has not proved very successful. One does not obtain clear speech by induction, unless one speaks close to the microphone. This means, therefore, that the microphone must be passed from one speaker to another, and at meal times or when sitting in the lounge at night, etc., this does not prove practical. If, as is normally done, the microphone is placed in the middle of the table or the middle of the room, then speakers are mostly so far away from it that the deaf person is not any better off than when wearing his ordinary hearing aid. Many parents who bought microphones and amplifiers in good faith are now trying to sell them again.

*** See End Notes p.27

Cros Aids

When a person has a significant hearing loss in one ear and either no hearing loss or a much less severe loss in the other ear (a unilateral loss), the hearing aid microphone is placed over the worse ear and the sound energy is transferred across the head to the better ear. An electrical cord is usually passed behind the head to make this transfer or it can be neatly concealed in the frame of spectacles. CROS stands for Contra Lateral Routing of Signals.

Sound produced on the side of the better ear is received at a slightly different time from that received by the microphone on the other side of the head. The hearing aid wearer thus obtains a degree of directional hearing that is not possible when listening with only one input..

There are also aids that use radio waves rather than wire to achieve this transfer of sound energy.

BI-CROS hearing aids have 2 microphones because the better ear also has a significant hearing loss. By placing microphones on opposite sides of the head from the receivers, a baffle is created that enables greater amplification to be used without so much likelihood of acoustic feedback occurring.

End Notes

*   A decibel is a unit of sound pressure. It is now always written as dB (without a fullstop).

**   A dyne is a unit force. One gram under the pull of gravity exerts a force of 980 dynes, at sea level and certain latitudes. (From Wever, EG - 1957 - Theory of Hearing, New York, John Wiley).
Physicists recently began using the much more accurate measure of sound pressure levels which are µPa. The zero on this scale is set at 20 µPa. The Pa commemorates the name of the eminent French mathematician, philosopher and physicist, Blaise Pascall (1623-1662). This remarkable scientist designed the first calculating machine - beginning an idea which was not fully developed for several centuries; he worked on the problem of vacuum; on the equilibrium of liquids and again was centuries ahead of his time in discussing the science of probability. In November, 1645 when 22 years old, Pascall had a religious "revelation" and never worked as a scientist again.

*** The RNID has a wide variety of information on *"Aids to Daily Living"* for deaf people. This list includes television listening devices such as a microphone or plug-in listening aids; amplified headphones; loop systems for use with hearing aids or without aids; louder or extension doorbells, etc. Parent-Teacher organisations are recommended to write to the RNID if advice is needed.

Helpful information on the above topics and innumerable other educational, audiological and social problems of deaf children and adults can also be obtained from the addresses given on pages 153 and 154 below. (So that these good people are not "flooded" with requests, it is suggested that parents and teachers might write through their Parent-Teacher organisations rather than as individuals and then distribute copies of the information received to their interested members.)

Chapter 2

THE MEASUREMENT OF HEARING

This chapter deals with the importance of testing; a description of pure tone and speech tests of hearing and a discussion of the various steps involved in a clinical test of a child's hearing.

The important subjects of screening tests for infants and school-aged children are discussed in Chapter 12. Immittance measurements to locate the source of middle ear disorders in children are described in Chapter 3.

Educationalists and psychologists are realising more and more the importance of keeping careful records of all aspects of children's abilities.

"To teach arithmetic to Richard or geography to George, it is not sufficient to know just the principles of arithmetic or the facts of geography. The teacher must also know Richard and George."

In addition to the documentation of educational, psychological, medical and social data, if one intends to obtain a full picture of a "deaf" child, it is very necessary to have an accurate assessment of his hearing for speech and for pure tones. It is not sufficient now to know just that a child is "deaf" or is "partially hearing". A teacher of a very deaf class should be able to think of each member of the group and say, for example, "Molly has a 100dB loss, yet she can do an amazing amount with the hearing she has retained, e.g., she can discriminate between five Dale-Haig words with dissimilar vowels, loves organ music, can detect quite slight changes in pitch and in rhythm, can identify me from the rest of my class by the quality of my voice, and always lets me know as soon as her hearing aid is not working. John, on the other hand, has a 95 dB loss, yet doesn't seem to have much discrimination at all - he has poor hearing for vowels, he can sometimes differentiate between sounds of widely dissimilar pitch, but as often as not gets quite confused. He doesn't like wearing his aid - quite understandably I suppose, etc.". When possessing such information for all the class, this teacher would never ask any child to do the impossible when directing his/her listening, nor would she waste time giving experiences of listening which are so easy for a child that they bored him or her. In addition, of course, this knowledge assists the teacher when she reviews individual progress. Although all the class may have very similar pure tone losses the amount of help that their hearing is likely to have been to them must be considered in relation to the other factors of age, intelligence, home background, etc.

In addition to the tests such as those described later, teachers should continually be asking themselves "I wonder if Billy can hear this, or Peter hear that?" and in this way be building up a more and more precise picture of each child's hearing capacity.

The Ewings emphasised the importance of hearing tests. "Without systematic tests there can be no guarantee of any measure of efficiency in procedures designed to help individual children, who are deaf, to enjoy ... the least imperfect experience of hearing that their residual capacity to hear permits."

There is considerable merit in one teacher's being responsible for all the pure tone and speech testing. This standardises procedures and the results can be compared between any two children throughout the school. Whilst this provides very useful reference data, there is a strong argument for class teachers doing much of their own *speech* testing. The harassed teacher who said "We're here to teach 'em, not to test 'em," had become a victim of a too rigorous application of evaluative techniques. Testing for testings' sake is never, of course, intended, but the most effective method for teachers to obtain the information they require about each child's capacity to hear is by their own careful individual testing (out of school time!).

How Frequently Should Hearing Tests Be Given In Schools And Classes For Deaf Children?
There seems to be no hard and fast ruling here, though most would agree that audiograms should be taken at least once each year. If any medical attention is given tests and measurements, are, of course, made much more frequently than this.

Hearing for speech tests should be made at the same time as audiograms are taken, and at other times as the class teacher sees fit.

PURE TONE TESTS

The Audiometer
The instrument designed to measure human hearing for pure tones is called the *audiometer* (Fig. 2:1). Usually audiometers determine the threshold of audibility of a subject at each octave. The instruments differ widely in shape and size, but all have two important controls which are used when a test is administered. The first sets the frequency of the tone to be tested, i.e., whether it is to be high or low in pitch. The second controls the *intensity* or loudness of the sound presented. As a test is made, a graph or *audiogram* is plotted which shows the

acuity of a subject's hearing over a range of frequencies (Fig. 2:2).

Fig. 2:1

A

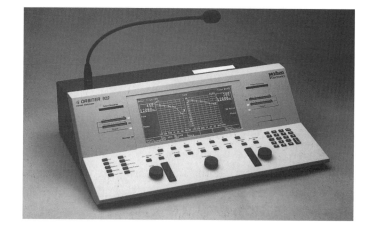

B

C

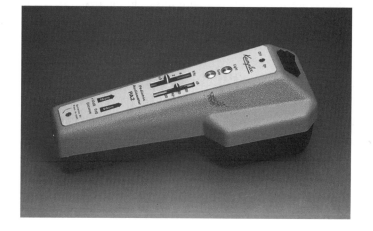

In Fig. 2:1, instrument A is a clinical audiometer which is useful to audiologists in administering a variety of diagnostic tests.

There are numerous types of audiometers available today. Really all that a school for deaf children or a unit in an ordinary school requires, is an instrument such as Audiometer B in Fig. 2:1. Such audiometers are capable of providing air and bone conduction thresholds; masking facilities and a useful speech circuit with output levels clearly marked in 5 dB steps.

School medical officers and general practitioners often carry small audiometers such as Audiometer C which are useful for basic screening testing. Children (and adults) who appear to have significant hearing losses are usually referred on to audiology clinics or to an otologist (ENT specialist) where more thorough diagnostic tests and examinations may be performed.

Health Department officers who are responsible for the screening of the hearing of a whole year group in their area, just require a robust air conduction audiometer and when a child fails a screening test, he or she is referred to an audiology centre for further investigation and treatment.

Audiometers have been found to require annual checking to ensure that they remain in calibration (Fearn[55] - 1976).

"Confusion and disagreement exist as to the preferred method for clinical determination of pure tone thresholds."[28] Carhart and Jerger went on to urge that audiometrists standardise their methods of testing hearing by adopting the basic features of the Hughson-Westlake technique.[81] This "ascending method" involves progressing from a level where the sound is inaudible to the first level where it can be heard, then dropping the intensity by 10 or 15 dB, and ascending again.

By 1981 the British Society of Audiology and the British Association of Otolaryngologists had agreed on recommended procedures for a variety of audiological tests. These included pure-tone air and bone conduction tests; air and bone conduction masking; tympanometry; establishing uncomfortable loudness levels, Rinne and Weber tuning fork testing, etc. These data were published in the Societies' journals in 1981 and are available from the British Society of Audiology's office at Harvest House, 80 Brighton Road, Reading, Berkshire RG6 1PS.

PURE TONE AUDIOGRAM

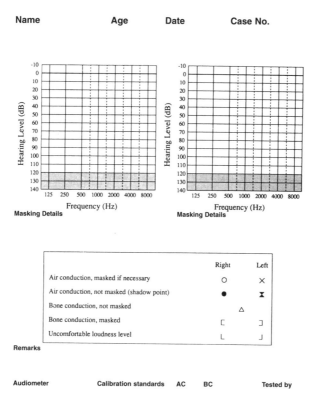

Name   Age   Date   Case No.

Fig. 2.2 British Society of Audiology and Association of Otolarnygologists' recommended audiogram form.

Children from 3-plus to 7 Years of Age
Steps in Testing

1. Check audiometer.
2. Establish rapport.
3. The "Go" game.
4. Hand-held audiometer or pitch pipe as stimulus
5. Audiometer headset.
6. Begin test at appropriate level and frequency.
7. "Down by tens and up by fives."
8. Record threshold.
9. Test other frequencies.
10. Is masking required?

1. *Check the Audiometer.* Before the first child of a testing session is asked into the clinic, quickly check your own hearing to ensure the audiometer is working satisfactorily.

2. *Establish Rapport.* Best results are obtained when the child feels happy and confident. Ways which may be used to promote this include:

    (a) Helping the mother to relax. It is often quite an ordeal for parent to bring their little children for a first hearing test and they need reassuring just as the child does. If a cup of tea or coffee can be provided for them on arrival at the centre, it frequently does a tremendous amount of good.

    (b) To have some coloured play apparatus in your hand when you ask the child into the testing room.

    (c) To glance briefly at the child and smile as he/she enters the clinic.

    (d) Smile at the mother also and let her know very briefly what course the session will take, e.g., "I'm just going to give Bobby a few tests, Mrs. Brown, and after that we'll have a good talk about him."

    (e) Help the child on to the chair. Such physical contact seems to promote a feeling of security in them.

    (f) Let the mother sit near the table if the child seems at all disturbed.

3. *The "Go" Game.* Obtain the child's co-operation in this simple activity.[57] It is often possible to delete a number of the preliminary steps. Instructions which are usually sufficient are as follows:

    Bobby, Mummy (or "Miss Jones" - the assistant) is going to play a little game. When I say "Go!" (or "Now!"), she will take one of these (pegs from the pegboard or a coloured block. See Fig. 2:3) and put it in here, (in a cardboard box lid or in the groove around the edge of the board). "You watch - Go! - Go!" etc. The child is encouraged to watch the tester's face as he or she ways the word. After three or four pegs have been moved, say "Now could you do that?" (For young children or those who seem unlikely to co-operate readily, a beat on a drum or chime bar should be used as the initial stimulus, and introduce "Go" or "Now" later.)

Fig. 2:3

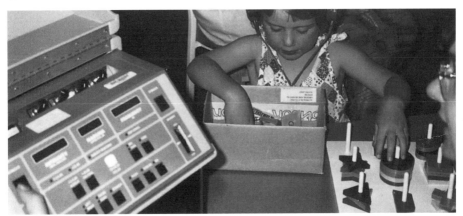

4. *Hand-held audiometer or pitch pipe as stimulus.* After several successful moves, say "That's good. Now watch Mummy (Miss Jones) play another game". Use a 1,000 Hz pitch pipe instead of saying "Go". (For children suspected of being very deaf, use a 500 Hz tone). Hold the hand-held audiometer or blow the pitch pipe near the child so that he has a good opportunity of hearing it as well as seeing the pitch pipe blown or the audiometer stimulus button depressed.

    When three or four trials have been completed, move behind the mother or the assistant and show that she can do the test without watching the tester. Vary the pauses between signals a little. "Now can you do that?"

5. *Audiometer Headset.* Place the headset of the audiometer on the assistant (or on yourself). Remember to smile as you do this since some children feel nervous at the sight of any such equipment. "Miss Jones is (or I am) going to listen to some more of those little whistles." Point to one ear phone and wait for a moment with a look of concentration on the face - suddenly smile and say "There's one", and move a peg on the peg board. Repeat this several times.

    Next place the headset on the child. If he seems worried, it is a good idea to let Mother listen first. (Very occasionally, some children are particularly nervous. With these, one can sometimes remove one receiver from the headset and hold it first against one's own ear, then to the mother's, and finally to the child's. In this way an approximate threshold can be obtained over a limited range of frequencies. Such children are usually very much more co-operative on a second test.)

6. *The First Tone.* The aim is to present a tone to the child which he can hear clearly and yet which is near his threshold and not so loud that it will disturb him. Begin the test at 1,000 Hz at 50 dB, if the hearing is likely to be near normal and at 70 dB, if there seems to be some hearing loss. If the child appears to be very deaf, begin the test at 500 Hz at a level of 70 dB. The signal should be not less than one second and not more than two seconds in duration.

7. *"Down by Tens and Up by Fives."* If a response is obtained, drop 10 dB, and test again. Quickly reduce the loudness in 10 dB steps until the child fails to respond, then increase in 5 dB steps. On obtaining another response, drop down 10 dB, and test up again in fives. The threshold for any frequency is the lowest level at which the child responds three times.

8. *Recording Thresholds.* The conventional symbols are "x" for the left ear and "o" for the right, the frequencies being joined by straight continuous lines.

Provided the audiogram used is a reasonable size, it is fairly general practice to record thresholds for both ears by air and bone conduction, on the one graph. No confusion results when one has become familiar with interpreting such audiograms, and comparisons between ears and between air and bone conduction curves are much easier. There is no necessity to use different colours for recording thresholds, nor to use an audiogram for each ear as is occasionally done.

9. *Test Other Frequencies*. There seems to be no definite ruling about the order in which the other frequencies are tested. One method is to continue from 1,000 to 2,000 and 4,000 and then go back to 250 and 500. There is little virtue in testing above 4,000 Hz and one can cause fatigue in the child by prolonging the test unnecessarily. If a child is proving difficult to test, try to get an estimate of the hearing loss at 500, 1,000 and 2,000 only - particularly 1,000 Hz in an initial test.

10. *Masking*. Finally, consider the curves obtained for both ears and ask yourself if masking need be applied (see below).

Children Over 7 Years of Age

With older children the approach is similar but it is not necessary to spend so much time in conditioning the child, nor in asking them to shift pegs or blocks, etc., when they hear a sound.

> *Instructions*. "Jean, you are going to hear some whistles like this ..." Blow 1,000 Hz or 500 Hz pitch pipe. "When you hear it, will you tap on the table with this pencil?' (Or alternatively, "will you raise your hand?") Demonstrate whichever response you require.
> Try first with the child watching and listening and then when listening alone (behind the subject but near the ear).
> "Now you are going to hear the same whistles through these", (place the audiometer headset on the child and test as for younger children).
> It is usual to test the better ear first and most children from seven or eight years of age can tell you which this is.

BONE CONDUCTION TESTING

(N.B. It is not now necessary to administer bone conduction tests to subjects who have normal immittance test results - see Chapter 3). Pure tone bone conduction tests are similar in administration to the air conduction tests just described. The following points should, however, be borne in mind:

1. The preliminary "conditioning" period ("Go" game, etc.) can be omitted

since bone conduction tests follow air conduction ones in the clinical session.

2. The bone conduction receiver must be very carefully placed on the mastoid process behind the ear. Ensure that there is no hair under the receiver, and that the head band is comfortable. Alternatively, place the bone conduction receiver on the middle of the forehead.

3. The audiometer is switched to bone conduction!

4. Only three frequencies should be tested - 500, 1,000 and 2,000 Hz.

5. Any responses in excess of 60 dB should be disregarded as these may be caused by the subject feeling a vibration on the skin.

6. Bone conduction tests are not regarded as being as reliable as air conduction ones.

Fig. 2:4. An audiogram showing air and bone conduction thresholds for left and right ears before and after 70 dB of 50 Hz band width and white noise masking had been applied to the right ear (see pp 37-39).

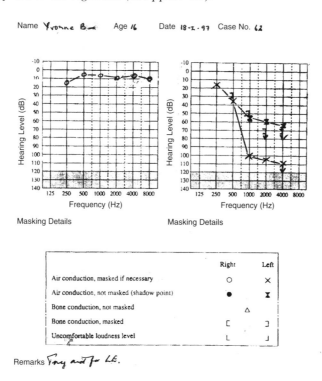

Name Yvonne B.   Age 16   Date 18-2-97   Case No. 62

Frequency (Hz)

Hearing Level (dB)

Masking Details   Masking Details

	Right	Left
Air conduction, masked if necessary	O	X
Air conduction, not masked (shadow point)	●	⚡
Bone conduction, not masked	Δ	
Bone conduction, masked	⊏	⊐
Uncomfortable loudness level	L	⌐

Remarks Tony and for LE.

Audiometer Blu   Calibration standards AC ✓ BC ✓   Tested by HH.

It is important always to bear in mind that masking may be necessary. In the case cited in Fig. 2:4, for example, if an aid was to be tried in the worse ear, an instrument with a quite different response might have been chosen.

Masking noises are of two types: *narrow band* and *white noise*. Just as white light is composed of all the colours in the spectrum, so white noise is a multi-frequency sound. It sounds like, and is sometimes described as, a "frying noise". It is extremely useful when masking sounds of 1,000 Hz, or higher. For sounds below 1,000 Hz, pure tone or 50 Hz band width masking is more effective when centred around the test frequency.

How Much Masking?

When using air conduction tests Zwizlocki[159] suggested that one should apply 45 dB of pure tone masking to the ear not being tested at the same frequency as the test tone. This level should be increased by 5 dB at each octave i.e., until 65 dB was used at 4,000 Hz. At 8,000 Hz Liden, et al (1959) recommended a masking level of between 45 and 80 dB.

Table 2:1

Suggested narrow band and white noise masking levels for pure tones
(Adapted from Zwizlocki[159])

Frequency in Hz	Masking Level Non-Test Ear	Type of Masking
250	45-75)	
500	50-75)	50 Hz band centred
1000	55-70)	around the test tone
2000	60-70)	
4000	65-75)	White Noise
8000	45-80)	

These data were calculated some 40 years ago, but apart from the fact that narrow band and white noise masking centred on the test tone is now recommended, rather than pure tones, the levels of masking remain much the same as the above levels of Zwizlocki and of Liden, et al.[98]

Masking should be applied to the better ear if the difference between the ears at any frequency is greater than 35 dB by air conduction and on every occasion when using bone conduction.

Over Masking. It is necessary to guard against over masking. If in the case shown in Fig. 2:4, for example, 90 dB of masking had been applied to the better ear, the patient would not have been able to hear sounds in either ear.

The skull is such an excellent conductor of sound vibration, that almost no energy is lost around the head when a bone conduction signal is applied to one ear. In consequence it can be perceived almost as well by the non test ear. For this reason it is not uncommon to place the bone conduction receiver on the middle of the patient's forehead and apply air conduction masking to the ear not being tested *on every occasion.*

Goldstein and Newman (1985) suggested clinical masking was a "complex and somewhat variable phenomenon". Despite that, one must persevere with its use for the important reasons given.

In 1986, the British Association of Audiology and the British Association of Otolaryngology published procedures which they hoped would encourage uniformity in the use of masking techniques for adults and older children in Britain. (See pg 31)

SPEECH TESTS OF HEARING

N.B. Students are recommended to read the whole of this section before attempting to administer any of the tests.
For years it has been said that "Pure tone and speech tests of hearing are the basis of clinical audiometry". Despite this, speech testing has not been routinely used by a number of audiologists and teachers when fitting hearing aids to children. "Lack of time" is the reason frequently given for this. With practice, however, speech tests can be administered quite quickly and efficiently.

Reasons for Administering Speech Tests of Hearing:

1. They help decide whether amplification is helpful. (A few children with hearing losses do not benefit from amplification and after a careful trial period for adjustment, they should not be asked to wear hearing aids. Such children are very rare, however, and most can be shown to benefit from experiencing sound.)

2. If only one hearing aid is worn, tests help to decide which ear to fit.

3. Which aid to select. It might not be the most expensive nor the most attractive. We must decide which aid enables a child to hear best.

4. Which frequency response achieves most intelligibility of speech material.

5. At which level of loudness the child obtains his/her maximum score on a speech test. (This is particularly important for young deaf children.)

6. Studying the improvement to the child's score when using a hearing aid can help convince reluctant wearers (especially if they are bright children), that one is better off wearing the aid. They can be told that it helps the teachers and the members of their family because these people don't have to repeat so many things when speaking to them.

7. Teachers and parents can obtain a much clearer picture of what sounds a child is likely to hear and when they are only "teasing" him/her with a listening test.

8. Music and television programmes can often become more enjoyable if children can be shown that they do have the ability to hear more of the sounds.

9. Some children improve considerably in word discrimination after becoming familiar with using the aid regularly. A comparison of initial and later scores on speech tests can be encouraging to these children.

It is not proposed here to review the development of all speech tests of hearing. This has been done adequately by Watson and Tolan, Hirsh[72], Palva[114], Harold[67], and others. An attempt will, however, be made to classify most of the speech tests according to difficulty and suitability for deaf children.

The most exacting speech hearing tests have proved to be the nonsense syllable type comprising consonant-vowel-consonant (e.g., wez, nad, gol, etc.), because in such tests it is almost essential to hear every sound in order to obtain maximum score (Fletcher).[58] Lists of monosyllabic words with adult vocabulary have been found easier than nonsense syllables. Due to the limited number of possible combination of sounds, a subject can frequently hazard a reasonable guess at the word said although he has heard only two of the three phonemes which comprise it. Such tests were constructed by Fry and Kerridge,[62] and at Harvard in 1944 by Hudgins *et al.*[78] An even less discriminating test is that of disyllabic words such as those constructed at the Central Institute for the Deaf (Hirsh).[72] Hirsh pointed out that since not all combinations of two syllables constituted words in English, the field of possible responses was further restricted. Finally, for subjects with normal vocabularies, sentence tests are probably the easiest of all the pure auditory discrimination speech tests. Fletcher and Steinberg[59] used lists of questions to which patients were required to give an answer.

Because of the limited vocabularies of the majority of children with impaired hearing, none of the above tests can be recommended for use in schools for the deaf or for such children in audiology clinics. In spite of this, it was a surprisingly long time before speech tests for such children were published. Numbers and Hudgins[112] adapted the Harvard lists for use in an American school for the deaf. In 1953, T.J. Watson[150] constructed his Manchester Junior (M/J) lists of monosyllabic words which were taken from the vocabularies of five year old Scottish children with normal hearing. He standardised them for use with English partially hearing children. See Appendix 2:3.

In spite of the simplified vocabularies of Hudgins' and Watson's[(Ibid)] tests, they found that they were too difficult for a large number of the more severely deaf children. Consequently, Quick, under the direction of Hudgins, constructed a simplified multiple choice type test which was administered with listening plus lip-reading. Watson compiled an easier test in which the child was presented with a set of twenty cards on each of which six pictures were pasted. The names were printed under each picture. One word on each card was from the test list. The child was required to point to one picture in response to the stimulus he heard.

The National Acoustic Laboratories of Australia developed a similar test which consisted of twenty-five words on each of five cards. Ten words were tested from each group. This test could be more quickly administered than Watsons[113] test, although, of course, a certain amount of accuracy was lost. The RNID published a similar screening test for use with children from about the age of seven years (Appendix 2:1). Four pictures of monosyllabic words containing the same vowel (e.g., fish, dish, pig, ship) were set out on each page of an eight-page booklet and the child (or adult) was required to discriminate between them when the four words were said in random order. Kendall[95] developed a simple test for young deaf children using sets of toys (Appendix 2:4 and Fig. 2:5). These lists originally contained ten test words and two distractors.

Fig. 2:5

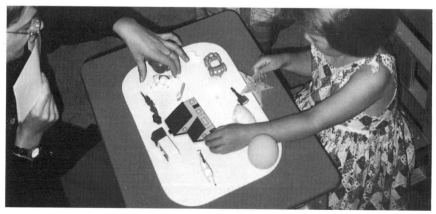

Harold adapted Watson's M/J lists (Appendix 2:6 and Fig. 2:6) so that they could be used for children with more severe impairments of hearing than had originally been intended. He placed ten words (and where possible pictures) on each card, five from one list and five from another. When testing, all five from one test were called and the five remaining words served as "dummies" or distractors.

ADMINISTRATION OF SPEECH TESTS

In speech tests of hearing, *instructions* are always given while the child is both looking and listening with his/her hearing aid if one is possessed.

The following speech tests are recommended for children of different ages and different degrees of deafness:

Fig. 2:6

school	egg	car	cup	ship
play	bird	duck	home	cake

Children Aged Between 7 and 12 Years

1. *RNID Hearing Test Cards.* Administration instructions are included. Especially useful to doctors, speech therapists, public health nurses and teachers for screening the hearing of children suspected of slight deafness (Appendix 2:1).

2. *M/J Words.* (Appendix 2:2). For children whose speech is quite intelligible. Very useful in audiology clinics.

Test 1. Instructions

(Given in a clear deliberate voice - the child watching the speaker.)

"I am going to read you some words and I want you to say the same word that I say - so if I say "boat" I want you to say "boat", if I say "three", I want you to say "three", and if I "horse", what would you say"? Give one or two more examples.

"Are you ready?" Read List 1, while the child watches and listens at the same time. If he/she has a body worn hearing aid it should be worn on the front of the chest. (After you have checked that it is working!) If an error is made by the child, or a word is not said at all, don't repeat it - go on to the next one. Note any errors. If the first ten words are said correctly, go on to Test 2.

Test 2. Instructions

"Now I am going to say some more words, but this time you will not be able to watch my face." Tester stands to one side, and slightly behind the child at a distance of one metre. List 2 is then read with the voice kept at a normal conversational level. If this is completed satisfactorily, go on to Test 3 or Test 4.

Test 3.

(If the child has a hearing aid).

Move in front again and say, "Now can you do the same but without your hearing aid?" Remove the aid, and stand one metre from the ear in which the child has been wearing it. Read List 3.

Test 4.

Move in front of the child again to give the instructions. "This time I am going to *whisper* the words so you will have to listen very carefully." Stand at the side and read List 3. (Be careful to whisper softly!).

Interpreting Results

(a) *Teachers in Ordinary Schools*: If a child scores 20 or less on Test 1 or Test 2, the principal of the school should inform the Medical officer of Health.

If a child appears to have a very slight deafness (say, five or less errors in Test 3), it is worthwhile to re-check the hearing again in a week's time, so that the medical people are not notified unnecessarily. If you are at all doubtful, however, the child should be referred.

(b) *Clinic Workers and Teachers of Deaf Children*: The speech test results should confirm the threshold obtained in the air conduction audiometric test.

As mentioned earlier, it is often possible to obtain scores when the child is tested with and without the hearing aid, which convince children that the aid *is* of benefit to them. It is not uncommon, for example, to obtain a percentage of eighty, aided, and perhaps twenty-four unaided (score in 25 words x 4).* It is relatively easy then to point out to the child that the aid should be worn regularly.

3.   *Adapted M/J Words.* For children with defective speech and whose hearing losses do not exceed 90 dB. (See Appendix 2:3).

Lists in book form (see Fig. 2:5), ten words per page for the first five pages, five words from List 1 and five from List 2. Next five pages compiled from Lists 3 and 4, and so on.

Test 1. Subject reads words on one page, and then watches and listens (with his hearing aid, or the audiometer headset), as words from List 1 are delivered. Child points to the word he thinks was said. All of List 1 is read, the words of List 2 acting as distractors.

Test 2. "Now can you do that without looking at me?" Read List 3 - being careful to give the child time to read the ten words on each page before the five being tested are delivered.

It is possible, with this test, to give a series of lists at different loudness levels and by comparing the scores obtained, to establish the best listening level for a particular child. It would be advisable to do this in those cases where the child chooses a level which seems very different from that suggested by Harold[69] for a child with his pure tone threshold.

Speech Tests for Children Aged 12-plus

(*a*)   *For Children Whose Speech Is Intelligible*: The words contained in the M/J lists are too easy for older children, i.e., the scores obtained are much higher than is reasonable if they are used with children from about twelve years of age, In consequence, the National Acoustic Laboratories' adaption of a test such as the MRC Word Lists are recommended (Appendix 2:3). These lists are administered in just the same way as the M/J lists described above.

(b)   *For Older Children Who Are Severely Or Profoundly Deaf,* the adapted M/J words and the Dale/Haig Vowel Discrimination Tests may be used (see below).

---

* See page 41.

Speech Tests For Young Children

1. *Kendall's Toy Test (K/T).* (Slightly adapted). For children with some
    vocabulary and a hearing loss not greater than about 85 dB. (See Appendix
    2:3).
    Kendall described a speech test which he devised for young deaf children.
    These tests have been used in the Centre for Audiology and Education of
    the Deaf at The University of Manchester, and elsewhere, for a number of
    years, and are extremely useful tests for the teacher or the clinician.

    Five lists, each of twelve paired monosyllabic nouns, were chosen
    (Appendix 2:3), and the lists were equated for difficulty.

    In administration, twelve toys, representing each twelve words, are placed
    in a box. The tester removes the first object, asking, "What's the name of
    that?" - "That's right. That's the horse - or spoon - or brush, etc." When all
    the objects have been named by the child, and spread in front of him, he is
    required to replace them in the box one by one when asked to do so. "Put
    the shoe in the box," "Put the key in the box," etc.

    It can be seen that as the test progresses, the number of objects on the table
    is reduced, so that the child is discriminating between fewer and fewer
    possible words, i.e., the test is becoming easier and easier. To counteract
    this a little, only the first ten words in each list are used in the test - the last
    two words being included as distractors.

    It is sometimes possible to ask the child to "Show me the ...", rather than to
    put it in the box, and in this way to keep the test of equal difficulty
    throughout. For the younger children, however, this never seems so
    successful as does the activity of putting the toys away.

    The tester must decide under what conditions this test is to be
    administered, depending on the apparent defect of the child. If the hearing
    loss appears to be very slight, the first list could be delivered at a
    conversational level - 60-70 dB, and for those with losses less than 90 dB,
    the first list may be given with the child watching and listening at one of
    the levels recommended by Harold (see Table 7:1 p101).

    The second test (List 2) could be given with the child listening without
    watching, and if this is successfully completed the level may be reduced in
    the successive tests until the child has difficulty in performing the test.

    If a mistake is made by the child, e.g., he puts the "cow" in the box when
    the word "house" was said, mark "house" as an error, and continue reading

the list, omitting the word "cow" when it comes, of course. Say, "Put the 'house' in the box" again at the end, but do not mark it as correct. Finally, put the toys out again and say, "Put the 'cow' in the box", (and any other words which have not so far been read). The number of words out of ten which were heard correctly are multiplied by ten to obtain the percentage.

This is a very useful test for school nurses, speech therapists, visiting teachers, doctors, etc., when wanting to screen the hearing of children in their first two years at school. It is attractive to little children, and the fact that the child is not required to speak, but simply to move an object, makes it easy for less confident children.

2.*Improvised Toy Test*. For very deaf young children, or those with very restricted vocabularies, the adapted K/T tests above are too difficult. it is necessary here to choose objects which are known to the child, and often to reduce the number of items used. Such modifications necessarily render the test less accurate, and they can at best be regarded as a crude estimate of a child's hearing for speech. They are useful, nevertheless, if carefully administered.

When making up such a test, choose words which are known to the child, and as far as possible have dissimilar vowels, e.g., boat, horse, car, tree, dog, might be suitable little list. None of the speech tests described above are satisfactory for the deafest children.

In consequence, in 1977, three speech tests of hearing were constructed by the writer and standardised by Haig in 1980[67]. (See Figs. 2:7, 2:8 and 2:9 below).

3. BKB lists for speech testing were constructed by Bench, Koul and Bamford in 1979 at the University of Reading and have proved useful.

Dale-Haig Vowel Discrimination Tests
All of these three tests are much easier than those which require listeners to discriminate words with different consonant sounds. They are recommended for children with hearing losses in excess of 90 dB. (Consonants are, of course, mainly high in frequency and low in intensity. (See Chapter 5).

The "bending" of vowel formants as the tongue and lips change the shape of the resonator (i.e., the mouth), also offer auditory clues to such severely and profoundly deafened children. Note, for example, the shape of the formants for the phoneme [u] in the word "took", for [u:] in "shoe" and [e] in "bench" in Fig. 5:6.

In addition to these and other acoustic factors, the number of items from which discriminations are to be made, also affects a subject's ability to discriminate between phonemes. (See Table 2:2 below).

In standardising the 3 tests on 80 severely and profoundly deaf children (Mean H.L. 100.06 dB, S.D. 12.05 db) aged between 7 and 16 means (Mean Age 11.88 years), Haig obtained the following data:

Table 2:2

	Test	Mean % Correct	S.D.
A	10 Vowel	29.01	20.13
B	5 Vowel	45.60	29.96
C	2 Vowel	57.20	20.13

(Friedman's Xr^2 = 97.775) which is, of course, highly significant statistically i.e., it can be safely assumed that the differences between the scores obtained on the 3 tests with this sample were significant and that Test A is more difficult than Test B and Test B is more difficult than Test C.

All of these words can be illustrated and it is recommended that teachers and audiologists, particularly with young children, should arrange the lists on cards beneath coloured drawings or cut out pictures (See Figs. 2:4, 2:5 and 2:6). If a child is unfamiliar with a word, that word becomes similar to a *nonsense syllable*. Although this is somewhat unfortunate, it is not "catastrophic" as these children are usually quite able to respond to the memory of the sound of the word which was given during the practice session. (Many teachers, who frequently know the children's vocabularies very well after a few weeks' teaching, can sometimes teach any unknown words in language sessions prior to the test).

These tests have proved suitable for use with children from 3+ years of age with profound hearing losses (Mean 90+ dB). In constructing the three tests, the writer endeavoured to meet the following criteria.

1. The vowel sounds had to be included in monosyllabic words (listening experiences need to be kept simple for such severely deaf children - uncluttered with unnecessary distractions as far as possible).

2. Each word had to be able to be illustrated. In addition to making the subtests more interesting for young children, older children were also helped by the pictures if they did not read well, or had restricted vocabularies.

3. The words had to be selected from the active vocabularies of 3 year old normally hearing children - i.e., a test of *auditory acuity* was required and not one of linguistic competence.

4. The 5 sub-tests of Test A and of Test B had to be equated for difficulty before standardising. Thus different scores on List A1 and A3 or List B2 and B5, for example, might be used to help establish output settings or which ear to fit, etc. It is emphasised, however, that when using so few words in each sub-test, several repetitions using different sub-tests over several days might be necessary to make final decisions.*

1. **The Ten Vowel Discrimination Test**

Fig. 2:7.

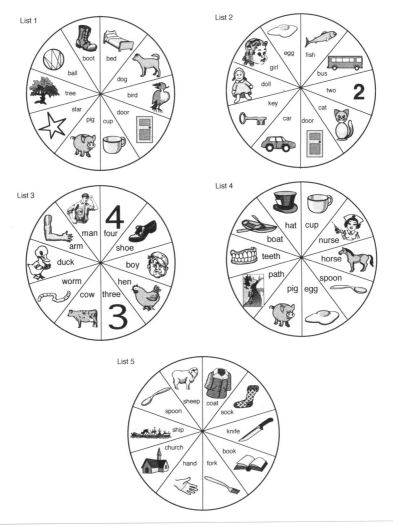

---

* Some slight changes have been made by the writer to the original lists to ensure that each word was able to be represented pictorially and was within the vocabulary range of 3 year old normally hearing children.

Administration:

Place List 5 in front of the child, smile and say "Do you know these words, Charles?". Allow the child to look at each word as you point with a pencil between each word and picture. Say each word quite deliberately and clearly as he/she looks at the word and then at your face. (Discourage children from speaking during this *listening* period.)

Next say "Now Charles (or "Judy" or whoever), if I say *"spoon"*, can you look around here and find it - like this?" Demonstrate, moving one's finger around the clock-face of pictures until one reaches the picture and word *"spoon"*, and say, (delightedly), "There it is!"

"Now, can we find 'coat'?" Again, move one's finger around the clock-face of pictures to the word 'coat' and smile with glee as one points to the picture and the word 'coat'.

"Now let's see you find this one - 'knife'." If this is performed correctly, give 2 or 3 more examples from List 5 and next say, "Now Charles, can you do the same, but with just "listening?". Touch the earpiece of the child's hearing aid and close one's eyes to indicate that he will not be able to look during this next test. After the child seems comfortable with this, i.e., has found 2 or 3 words correctly, he is ready to begin the test on List 1. Put List 5 away and place List 1 in front of the child. "First Charles, just *listen* to these."

Repeat the "training period" as with List 5, but move quite quickly around the 10 words, saying them deliberately as one points between each word and its picture.

Say: "Now are you ready Charles?" Smile, pause a moment, and then say the first word of List 1. The rest are delivered in random order, e.g., not, of course, just repeating all the words around the clock-face.

When a word is identified correctly, smile, mark 2 on the score sheet and move on to the next word. Repeat this process until all 10 words have been tested.

On the score sheet, add up scores obtained and multiply them by 10 to obtain a percent correct.

Administration may be first with Looking and Listening, second with Listening Only and finally at varying listening levels; with different hearing aids; with and without aids; with 2 aids or monaurally, etc. These tests should be repeated over several days to obtain accurate data and more than one list should be used on each test if one hopes to calculate each child's hearing for speech accurately.

2.   *The Five Vowel Test*

This test consists of 5 lists of 5 monosyllabic words. Each of these 5 words contain a different long vowel and these are arranged in random order in each list. (Long vowels are easier for deaf children to perceive and to discriminate between 5 phonemes is easier than between 10 - Haig[65] Ibid .)

Fig. 2:8

Administration
Place the test in front of the child, with Lists 1-4 covered.

Tester: "(Name of child), do you know these words?" Indicate List 5 and after a brief look, go straight on, indicating each word as it is said clearly within 10cm of the microphone of the child's hearing aid. "... tree, two, path, bird and fork."

With the child listening and looking, say, "Now (Name), show me the 'path'". If this is successful, smile, nod and say "Good, now watch, "tree" next "fork", "bird" and finally "two". "Good, now let's try *without looking*". After a pause, test each word again in random order when the child is listening only.

If successful, administer Lists 1, 2, 3, 4 and 5 and record results.

3. ***The Paired Vowel Test.***

Designed for extremely deaf children, this test consists of 10 pairs of 20 monosyllabic words which contain 5 pairs of long vowel sounds and 5 pairs of short vowels (Fig. 2:9). Children who do not know the names of some of the objects shown here, must regard such words as nonsense syllables. They are, however, still able to respond to the sound of the word - if, of course, they perceive it.

It is possible to teach quite young children to perform this test after a little practice. (Work for example, from the "Go game" technique.) Teachers in nursery classes have a good opportunity to do this if they are able to give a little individual work with their children each day. Audiologists who do not normally see the children daily, can often seek the class teachers' assistance. (Most are delighted to help!)

Fig. 2:9

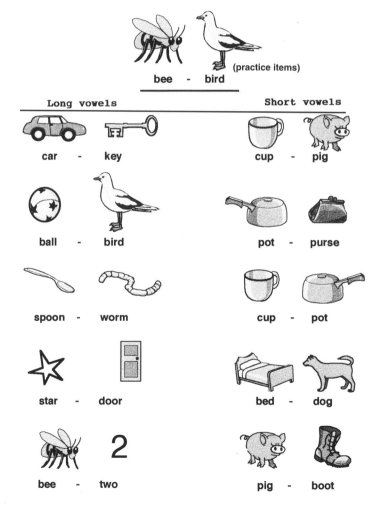

bee	-	bird	(practice items)	

Long vowels			Short vowels	
car	-	key	cup - pig	
ball	-	bird	pot - purse	
spoon	-	worm	cup - pot	
star	-	door	bed - dog	
bee	-	two	pig - boot	

Administration
Paired Vowel Test. **Place the full test in front of the child. After letting him/her look briefly at all the words, cover all but the practice items at the top with a sheet of paper.**

Next, while the child both looks and listens, say "(Name of child), can you *listen*" (as one taps the receiver of the child's hearing aid) "while I say these words?" Immediately point to the picture of the bee and say, "That's bee." Next point to the bird and say "and that's bird".

"(Name of child), can you show me - 'bee'; 'bird'; 'bird'; 'bee'; 'bird'?", i.e., enabling the child to see that the words may be said in random order.

(A number of children will think that they are expected to say each word after the tester. In such cases, the tester should gently press his/her finger to the child's lips, shake his/her head, and with a smile, say "No, I shall talk, and you just listen" (at the same time tapping the receiver of the child's hearing aid).

Next uncover the first pair of words and the test can begin as follows:

Tester: "(Name of child) will you listen to these words?" Words are said clearly as the tester also points simultaneously to each word, e.g., car - key, car - key, key - car, car - car, key - key. "Now, can you do that?" Repeat test as above.

Scoring. If the child points to each word correctly he/she scores 2 points: (Each word of each pair is repeated 5 times in random order). If an error is made, stop the test immediately and retrain the child as before. Remember that 1 point has been lost. If, on resuming the test, a further error is made, discontinue the test of that pair, and go immediately to training the next pair, i.e., ball - bird and score no points for the first exercise. At the conclusion of the tenth pair, add all of the points scored and multiply by 5 to obtain a percentage correct. If a profoundly deaf child can obtain a 30 percent correct score, it is felt that it is well worth him/her persevering with a hearing aid. It is also both possible and desirable to make modifications to the original test to ascertain whether significant improvements can be achieved. Which hearing aid seems most satisfactory? Which ear to fit? (If only one aid is to be worn.) What level of loudness appears to be optimum for this child? Who's voice is most intelligible? These are all questions that can be answered by the careful application of such tests (often over several days).

With practice, these tests can be quite quickly and accurately administered and the value of their findings to the children, their parents, teachers, speech therapists and audiologists make their use extremely worthwhile.

CLINICAL AUDIOMETRY

There are six steps in a normal clinical session for children from about the age of three and a half years when immittance measures are not being made. (See Chapter 3.)

(1)   Careful study of any case notes available.
(2)   Pure tone air conduction tests.
(3)   Speech tests.
(4)   Bone conduction tests.
(5)   Discussion with parents.
(6)   Diagnosis and recommendation.

Case Notes

Letters of referral are sometimes not very helpful. "Would you please see this child with regards deafness?" is often all that the letter contains. Before a child comes to an audiology clinic, however, it is usually very useful to know certain things about him. How old is he? Is his home a 'good' one? Has he been tested before? If so, what were the results?" If he is at school, what his headteacher says of his attainments and general adjustment? What special facilities are available in his area?

If you have been give no indication of how deaf the child is, you may be inclined to ask the mother as soon as she enters the clinic - "Do you think John is very deaf?" or "Well, what do you think is the problem?" The only snag in so doing, is that many mothers once started are sometimes difficult to stop! Quite understandably, they are often very worried about their child and are keen to tell all they know. It is most important that they be given the opportunity to do this before the end of the session. It is important also, however, that one gets on as quickly as is possible with the testing. The child can become bored with sitting doing nothing and may start exploring the clinic, or may become nervous and unable to co-operate in the tests when he is finally asked to do so. For these reasons some testers prefer to ask no questions at all at the beginning of a session, others are more specific in their questioning, e.g., "Do you think John has a severe or a slight hearing problem?"

Pure Tone Air Conduction Tests

With experience, one should be able to move quickly and smoothly through the steps which lead up to the audiometric test. It is important that time is not wasted on these so that the child begins the test with a minimum of fatigue.

Points to watch when administering an audiometric test include:

(a) The length of the stimulus sound. The signal should be presented for approximately two seconds. If they are of shorter duration than this, particularly when nearing threshold, they can be ignored by the child. They should not be continued too long, and if the subject begins to move a peg in the pegboard, or to tap the table before the two seconds is up, the tester should discontinue the signal.

(b) The time between any two signals should be varied occasionally, but it can be quite short.

(c) With little children, a change of activity is often useful in maintaining interest, e.g., they can take the pegs from the pegboard, next build and take down a tower of locking blocks, then make a pyramid from plastic rings etc., and finally replace the pegs in the board.

Speech Tests of Hearing

(a) In administering speech tests, always work from the most easy condition to the more difficult. For example, severely deaf children should look and listen with aided hearing first, then with aided hearing only, and finally with unaided hearing alone. In this way, they feel much more confident than if asked to do the most difficult test first. Similarly children who appear to be only slightly deaf should be given their first speech test at say 80 dB, and then the speech should be reduced to quieter levels.

Fig. 2:10

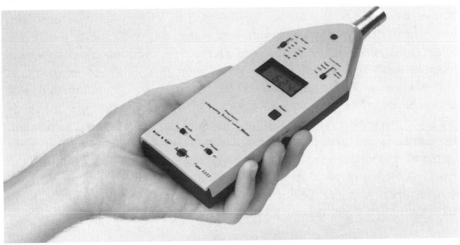

(b) The speech should be monitored either by using the speech circuit of an audiometer or speech training aid, or by means of a *sound level meter* if the tests are made free field. (Fig. 2:10)

It is most important in the latter case to ensure that the sound level meter is placed in the correct position before the test is begun (Fig. 2:11).

Fig. 2:11

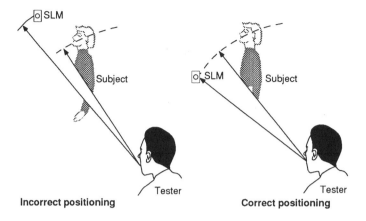

Incorrect positioning   Correct positioning

The microphone of the meter should be the same distance from the speaker as is the ear of the subject being tested. This may be achieved by the tester or a colleague holding the meter, or by the child holding it.

(c) Recorded or live voice? For older children and adults, recorded lists of words are very useful and more scientific than live voice tests. Identical test conditions can of course be obtained more nearly by using recorded material than is possible when lists are read by the tester each time - no matter how skillful he or she may be.

Despite this, live voice tests, provided they are well administered, have very many advantages. They are more personal than are recorded tests. The tester can thus deliver a word at precisely the moment that seems most suitable to the child, e.g., there is less likelihood of a child having to wait for a word or of receiving a word before he is ready for it. Some children respond quite quickly to the test words, others, particularly cerebral palsied children for example, require much more time to reply or to identify the word said. A test which is found to be too easy or too difficult can be discontinued at any point and a more suitable test administered without delay - with recorded material difficulty is sometimes experienced in finding the exact place required on the tape or the disc - and if this is not so, the technique is necessarily more time consuming than when live voice is used.

In my own experience live voice testing has proved very satisfactory in administering speech reception tests.*

---

* Animation is always important when teaching or talking to very deaf children, but one should neither "overact" nor "over-exaggerate" lip movements. The writer recalls one rather dejected student teacher coming out of a class of teenaged children who, he said, had all laughed when one of them had commented, "Your name - Mr Rubberface!"

Bone Conduction Tests

(a)   There is no hard and fast rule about the order in which speech tests and bone conduction tests should be administered. If a child has tested quickly and reliably by air conduction, one can frequently go straight on to test by bone conduction. If however, the air conduction test has been somewhat prolonged, and there have been signs of fatigue, it is often advisable to insert the speech tests to give the child a break from that type of activity.

(b)   It is usually a good idea to tell the child, "This test won't take long."

Discussion With The Parents

By the time the tester is ready to make a diagnosis and a recommendation he has usually built up a fairly accurate estimate of the child's ability to hear. As one becomes familiar with deafness and the handicap which varying degrees of it impose on children, one is able to estimate with fair accuracy what the effect of a given impairment will be. When this is considered in relation to the other known factors of intelligence, home background, special services available, it is usually possible to suggest what type of educational therapy is likely to produce the best results.

In diagnosis, one problem when speaking or writing to speech therapists, doctors, etc., is to find a satisfactory means of describing the hearing loss. To say for example that a child "has an auditory impairment in his left ear of 65 dB." means almost nothing to the majority of laymen. For this reason, such terms as "slight but not significant hearing loss," "slight but significant...," "partial hearing," "severe deafness," can be useful but with examples of what such children are often able to hear, e.g. a child with a hearing loss of 80 dB. might be described as "a severely deaf child -- she hears next to nothing of speech when it is at an ordinary conversational level; when using a hearing aid, however, she is able to hear 50 per cent of simple speech material (single words) correctly...." Again a child whose hearing loss is in excess of 100 dB. could perhaps be described as "a profoundly deaf child -- she is able to hear voice but only when it is made at the level of a shout very close to the ear;" and so on.

Recommendations

Unless you are a doctor or an otologist, it is advisable to preface every recommendation with "If nothing can be done to improve this hearing loss,..." (If writing to the family doctor or to an otologist, the phrasing might be "If this impairment proves irreversible..."). It should be emphasised that although an audiologist is justified and indeed is expected to diagnose the extent of a person's deafness on a given day, he is not qualified to make any suggestions about causation or even whether the deafness appears to be conductive, sensori-neural or mixed in origin. (Although, of course, through the shape and relationship of the air and bone conduction thresholds, one frequently has a fair idea.)

Chapter 3

ACOUSTIC IMMITTANCE

The term "immittance" is used in relation to *admittance* and its reciprocal, *impedance* when it is desired to refer to both functions without making a distinction between them.*

The work of Metz in 1946 with normal and pathological ears is felt to have given the impetus to subsequent development of measurements in auditory immittance.

The first immittance unit was introduced commercially in Denmark in 1957. In 1975, Jerger[86] and then Liden and associates classified tympanograms according to the shape which was typical or representative of particular conditions of the middle ear. These configurations and some others are still used today in interpreting immittance measurements. (See Fig. 3:1 and Brooks' 101 typical tympanometric traces Fig. 3:3 below.)

Immittance measurements assess the degree to which sound energy is enabled to enter the middle ear and the cochlear. They have been described by James Jerger as "one of the most powerful individual tools available for the diagnosis of auditory disorders". These measures are able to detect with great sensitivity the difference between cochlear and middle ear pathologies and can also determine overall hearing sensitivity with a high degree of accuracy as a cross check on pure tone audiograms. Immittance measurements do not require the child's active participation and hence are especially helpful in the difficult-to-test cases.

The acoustic impedance meter (Fig. 3:1), has a headset which holds a probe tip and this fits snugly into the ear. Air pressure changes can be introduced into the chamber so created (Fig. 3:2). Through this probe tip, 3 channels enter the sealed off outer ear.

Channel 1 carries one probe tone - often of 220 Hz. Some of this pure tone's energy will pass through the middle ear and some will be reflected. The amount of the tone reflected depends upon the stiffness of the middle ear mechanism.

Channel 2 carries air from a pump, either into or out of the sealed off chamber of the outer ear. This regulating of the air pressure in the chamber pushes the ear drum inwards or draws it outwards. Between these two extremes, when the

---

* The Compact Edition Oxford English Dictionary - Oxford, Clarendon Press 1997

56

pressure is the same as that of atmospheric air (0mmW.), the ear drum remains flat, i.e. in its most relaxed (or compliant) state.

Fig 3:1

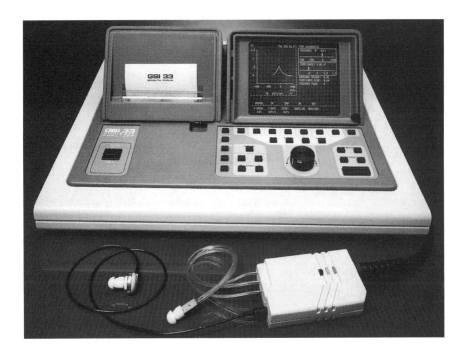

Fig. 3:2

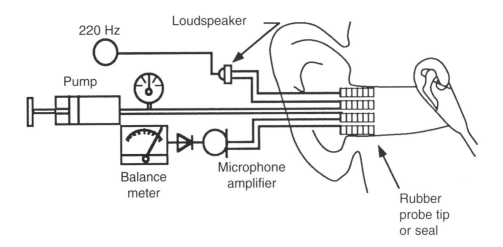

Channel 3 carries the reflected probe tone signal back to a balance meter (Fig. 3:2. An approximate analogy regarding the amount of sound reflected from the middle ear might be that of throwing a tennis ball at a concrete wall and at a trampoline that has been placed on its side. From the wall, the ball would return very smartly, but from the trampoline, much more slowly. In the case of severe otosclerosis where the footplate of the stapes has been almost completely immobilised, the sound would reflect rapidly from the ear drum which has been kept almost rigid. In a normally functioning middle ear, the sound would move the ear drum inwards and it would return more slowly.

To take this improbable analogy a little further, if the trampoline had a hole in it, the tennis ball would pass right through and would not come back! This is the case with a ruptured ear drum when acoustic impedance testing cannot be applied since it is not possible to obtain a seal.

One has also to be careful when inserting the probe tip in the ear canal, that gaps are not left at the sides which allow air to escape. If the probe tip chosen is too small or too large or the ear canal is not sufficiently circular in shape, air will escape and this can sometimes mistakenly be attributed to the presence of a rupture in the ear drum or some other malfunction.

Three measures of acoustic impedance/admittance are taken: the first when the ear drum has been stiffened by the withdrawal of air (200 millimetres of water pressure or 200mmW) from the sealed off chamber of the outer ear; the second when the middle ear is most relaxed, i.e., when the air pressure on either side of the ear drum is equal; and third, when 200mW of air has been pumped into the sealed off ear chamber. (Fig. 3:2).

The difference between the most and the least compliant state of the tympanic membrane or tympanum (i.e. 0mmW and + or - 200mmW), gives a measure of relative compliance. It is measured in c.c. of equivalent air volume as these are easier to manipulate than impedance units (which are measured in acoustic admittance ohms*). In Fig. 3:2, for example, the difference in volume of the outer ear chamber of the ear canal when the drum is fully extended and when it is at rest, is equivalent to about 3 c.c. in adults.

Northern observed that "the evaluation of hearing disability in children had become considerably less traumatic for audiologists" since the advent of immittance measurements which do not, of course, require the subject's active co-operation.[111]

Immittance measurements are used routinely in audiology clinics today. Tympanometry uses air pressures which range from + and - 200mm H^2O. See

---

* G.S. Ohm was the German physicist (1784-1857) who first measured these units of electrical resistance.

Fig. 3:3 for examples of various tympanogramic traces which are typical of different middle ear conditions.

Fig. 3:3

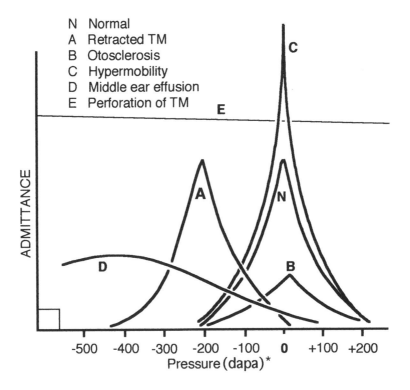

The tympanic membrane (ear drum) has been found to function best (have most elasticity) when the air pressure on either side of it is equal.

To maintain this equal pressure, air is enabled to pass up or down the Eustachian tube (tuba Eustachi - Fig. 8:1) each time the person swallows. Boiled sweets which are offered by some airlines as aircraft descend, cause passengers to swallow much more frequently than normal and by so doing, to open their Eustachian tubes more often. These tubes, of course, run between the middle ear and rear wall of the nasopharynx. Without the frequent swallowing, just one adjustment of the air pressure in the middle ear to that in the aircraft, can be more sudden and somewhat disturbing when one finally does swallow. Fellow passengers can sometimes be heard exclaiming with varying degrees of amusement, annoyance and even alarm "My ears have just popped!".

---

* dapa is an abbreviation of dacapasalls, i.e. hundredths of one pascal

Fig. 3:4

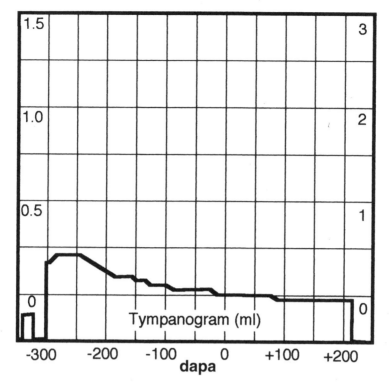

The tympanogram shown in Fig. 3:4 illustrates a typical plot for a case of *glue ear*. As Freeland[61] has pointed out, the ear drum is prevented from moving no matter what the pressure applied since the middle ear is full of viscous fluid.

As suggested above the technique for measuring the movement of the tympanic membrane depends on sealing the outer ear canal and then varying the pressure of air that has been trapped between the seal and the ear drum (see Fig. 3:2). With ear canals varying in shape and with a variety of different earplugs, hermetic sealing is not always easy. (It accounts for the audiology student's prayer the night before her practical examination which concluded: "... and tomorrow morning, dear Lord, please do help me get a seal.")

Immittance instruments have been developed which enable measurements of the function of the tympanic membrane with very considerable accuracy (see Figs. 3:3 and 3:4).

It is re-emphasised, however, that no one measure of acoustic immittance should be taken alone. As J.F. Jerger has pointed out, "The clinical value of immittance measurements lie in the unique interaction between the audiogram, the tympanogram and the acoustic reflex threshold".

Jerger, in 1975, believed that no new development in clinical audiology over the previous decade had such a profound effect as the advent of immittance measurement. Within that time, he noted that the measurement of immittance characteristics had developed from being a sophisticated research tool to "a clinical procedure applicable to virtually every patient referred for audiological examination".

Metz, in the mid-1940's, using an electro-mechanical method to detect changes in the acoustic impedance of the middle ear, was able to show that in patients with nerve deafness and loudness recruitment, contraction of the stapedius muscle could be elicited by sounds at considerably lower sensation levels than was the case in the normal ear. Much pioneering work on immittance measurements continued during the 1950's and 1960's in Scandinavia (Jepson, Terkildsen, Moller, Liden, et al).

Following on from the work of Terkildsen and his colleagues, Brooks in England and Alberti in Canada during the 1970's were able to show that immittance measurements could be made not only with adults but also with young children. Workers are now able to identify with accuracy and objectivity, most forms of middle ear disorders. Some English otologists, however, have indicated to the writer recently that they were not ecstatic about such measurement and results. Unless they were used in conjunction with inspection and pure tone audiograms. They cautioned, as Jerger had indicated, that there were, indeed, pitfalls in using immittance measurements alone for diagnoses.

It has been shown that immittance (and otoacoustic emissions) tests can be administered with accuracy to some children from as young as the first day after birth (see Fig. 12:1).

The Acoustic Reflex, (sometimes known as the stapedius muscle reflex). To test stapedius reflexes in one ear, it is necessary to administer an abrupt loud tone to the other. For normally hearing subjects, the average reflex threshold is 85 dB though some subjects react at 70 dB while others require 100 dB.

In addition to helping with diagnoses of conductive pathologies, stapedius reflexes to pure tones can be extremely useful for diagnosing:

1. *Loudness recruitment*: (See Chapter 8 for discussion of recruitment.) The stapedius reflex seems dependent on subjective loudness, so that reflex testing provides an objective test of recruitment, and is therefore an indicator of cochlear pathology. The implications of the recruitment phenomenon are that as long as sensori neural hearing does not exceed 60 dB, there is a 90% probability that a reflex will be present in one ear

with cochlear pathology. As the sensori neural loss increases above 60 dB, the likelihood decreases.

2.   *Facial palsy*: Stapedius reflexes will be present if the lesion of the 7th nerve is beyond the stapedius branch and absent if it is before.

3.   *Reflex decay*: In cases of 8th nerve involvement, where stapedius reflexes can still be obtained, the amplitude of the reflexes show definite decline over time. (Compliance changes are usually halved after 3 seconds' exposure to the eliciting sound.) 1000 Hz is the tone most frequently used to measure reflex decay.
Reflex decay is tested by presenting the tone for 10 seconds and observing the change in compliance on the balance meter or an XYT recorder. A 50% or more decrease in this time is taken as strong evidence of retrocochlear pathology.
Absent reflexes where there is no conductive hearing loss and insufficient hearing impairment to cause this, are also indicative of retrocochlear pathology and are regarded as a more reliable indicator than traditional audiometric tests.

4.   *Non-organic hearing loss*: When average stapedius reflexes are obtained at less than 85 dB, after a severe loss of hearing has been reported, NOHL is often indicated.

Immittance testing is used in a number of countries now as a screening instrument in schools. It has proved useful in detecting otitis media in children who have passed conventional pure tone screening tests of hearing. It is more reliable than bone conduction testing and is sensitive to an air-bone gap as small as 3 dB.

It is thus not necessary now to perform bone conduction tests on any subjects who are shown to have satisfactory immittance test results.

With its ability to provide objective information in cases of cochlear and retrocochlear involvement; to detect and diagnose conductive losses which are neither visible nor otoscopically functional deafness and facial nerve involvements, and finally to assist in the diagnosis of difficult-to-test children, immittance measurements have represented the most significant advance in audiology for many years.

ACOUSTIC REFLEX THRESHOLD

The acoustic reflex threshold is defined as 'the lowest possible intensity needed to elicit a middle ear muscle contraction". Northern[111] has stated that "The diagnostic implications of the acoustic reflex considerably outweigh the contributions of tympanometry and static compliance measurement".

The tiny muscle attached to the stapes contracts when a pure tone of between 70 and 100 dB. HTL is presented. This is thought to be a safety mechanism to prevent sudden sound pressure entering the cochlear and causing undue disturbance and damage to the hair cells.

It is interesting that the stapedius muscles contract in both ears even when only one ear has been stimulated. The lowest signal intensity capable of eliciting the acoustic reflex is recorded as the *acoustic reflex threshold* for the stimulated ear.

Acoustic reflexes become less and less likely to occur as the subjects' sensorineural hearing loss exceeds 60 dB. At 85 dB acoustic reflexes can be elicited in only about 50 percent of cases and at 100 dB HTL this is reduced to 5 or 10 percent.

In two significant articles, Keith, in the early 1970's showed that immittance measurements could be made accurately with babies from an extremely early age (see Fig. 12:1).

He established that all three tests of immittance could be administered with accuracy to infants from as early as their first day of life. Although there have been problems, Northern (1978) reported in detail, extremely helpful techniques for use when employing such measures with babies during "the first few weeks of life". He found normally hearing infants were easy to test.

For classroom teachers of deaf children, the significance of immittance measurements is not so great as for advisory teachers of the deaf, audiologists and otologists who deal much more frequently with children whose deafness is conductive in origin. (When one compares annual pure tone hearing tests of deaf and partially hearing children who have been attending special schools and classes, for example, one is frequently impressed by the stability of each child's pure tone hearing threshold over a period of several years in nearly every case.)

A few children in these schools and classes *do*, of course, have middle ear deafness in addition to their sensori-neural losses. These should be attended to expeditiously. Daily aural toiletting is recommended when ears are suppurating and when parents are unable to offer assistance, teachers are sometimes asked by public health nurses to undertake this task (after being shown what is required).

Hearing aids should never, of course, be placed in suppurating ears.

When the conductive deafness is caused by some other condition e.g., otosclerosis or discontinuous auditory ossicles, hearing aids may be worn. If the sensori-neural deafness is severe, however, few hearing aids will be effective. For example, with a loss of 90 dB and perhaps 30 dB of conductive deafness added to this, the degree of hearing loss becomes beyond the reach of most hearing aids. (The problem of preventing acoustic feedback also becomes particularly difficult to eliminate in such cases.)

Non Organic Hearing Loss (NOHL): (Sometimes called *functional* or *feigned* hearing loss or *malingering*.)

Occasionally children present with hearing difficulties which are subsequently found to be non-organic in origin i.e., the loss is imaginary or feigned rather than real. Sometimes this occurs after a child has had a slight hearing loss due, for example, to otitis media occurring during an attack of influenza. The subject subsequently feigns or exaggerates a hearing loss to retain the sympathetic concern of this family and/or his teachers.

Immittance measurements that do not agree with levels found in air or bone conduction tests, can indicate that malingering may be a cause of the incorrect levels earlier obtained.

Not infrequently, children with non-organic hearing losses are indicating that they need more attention and perhaps affection than they have been receiving. Parents and teachers should look carefully for reasons when this behaviour is manifest and should adopt a sympathetic approach rather than a punitive or scornful one.

Barr[5], in 1963 examined no less than 32 school children in Sweden whose hearing losses of between 60 and 80 dB did not equate with their almost normal hearing for speech. Overall, these children were of good average intelligence, but they had deliberately failed the school screening tests of hearing to help them account (to their parents and teachers) for their poor results in school examinations.

Children who are malingering can become quite skillful at explaining, for example, their exceptional ability in *lip-reading* and understanding spoken language.

In the early 1960's one such *profoundly deaf* 13 year old laughed at a remark made by the writer to an otologist, although the child's back was turned. When queried about this he said that he had been lip-reading our conversation from the reflection in the clinic window. No speech tests of hearing were possible with this child, because he insisted he was completely deaf and had to rely exclusively on lip-reading .

This subject ultimately "regained his hearing" after the (ingenious) otologist told him that he believed he had a rare type of profound deafness which was a form from which people could recover completely - "not immediately, but perhaps in a few months". Six months later the delighted parents commented that the boy was very proud of the article which had appeared in their local newspaper entitled "Hearing Miracle", and he carried it in his wallet "everywhere". Perhaps he still does!

Prior to this "complete recovery", for more than 2 years, this child had led his parents, teachers, specialist teachers of the deaf and school medical officers "a merry dance" when he vowed that he had "no measurable hearing" following a bilateral middle ear infection.

Northern and Downs[110] (1974), however, rightly suggested that "the apparent hearing loss may indeed be a silent cry for help" and that audiologists should not take such behaviour lightly. "Listen to his need" they urged. Lehrer, et al. (1964) had earlier reported "an excellent response" to psychotherapy programmes arranged for 10 teenaged children identified with non-organic hearing loss.

Brooks and Geoghegan[20], however, emphasise that most studies of NOHL have viewed the outcome of treatment only in "the relatively short term".

These workers, as well as Chaiklin and Ventry[29], enquired whether the initial resolution of the subjects' NOHL was permanent. Frequently, they felt that the condition which caused the problem of feigning hearing loss, did not disappear once the subject agreed that his/her hearing had returned to within normal limits.

Brooks and Geoghegan's follow up study of 28 malingerers after an average of 14 years, also ascertained that for only 11 of the patients were there "no significant findings"[20]. For example, 5 had speech problems, 6 had reverted to having a non-organic hearing loss and 6 had been referred for psychiatric or psychological assistance.

These writers agreed with the earlier workers that non-organic hearing losses should be taken seriously. They disagreed frankly with the recommendation of one English education authority which advised visiting teachers of deaf children to remove all NOHL children from their case loads and that "no further action should be taken with these children by any branch of the special education service". They should, however, certainly be kept on the educational psychologists register.

Tests of non-organic hearing loss in children include the most common one used by Barr[6] above, of noting discrepant pure tone and speech test results. Widely different findings immediately suggest that a non-organic hearing loss might be present. (This is provided, of course, that factors such as unfamiliarity with the language of the test or an aberration in the speech circuit of the audiometer have been ruled out.)

The use of *delayed speech*, where the voice of the subject reading a piece of prose, is played back to him/her approximately .2 of a second after each word is spoken, has a quite *devastating* effect on the speech of a person with normal hearing. (In the case of a subject with a significant hearing loss, however, no interference occurs because they are unable to detect the delayed speech.)

Pure tone audiograms which are "saucer shaped" can indicate non-organic hearing loss as these reflect normal psychoacoustic thresholds.

Bekesy audiometry results which do not follow the level of loss indicated by the speech test results and a pure tone test administered earlier will also arouse the tester's suspicion.

Continuous Bekesy tracings which are at less severe levels than interrupted tones are felt by audiologists to be clear indications of non-organic hearing loss.

Voice quality and speech production: Although indicating that they have acquired a significant hearing loss, malingerers frequently do not reflect this in their subsequent speech production. In the case of genuinely acquired deafness, the consonant sounds and blends soon become less distinct and severe deafness affects both the quality (*timbre*) of the voice and also the ability to regulate its intensity in noisy or quiet conditions. In malingerers, such characteristics are seldom manifest.

Recommended Reading:

Ballantyne, D. (1990) *Handbook of Audiological Techniques*, London, Butterworth-Heinemann.

Jerger, J. & Hayes, D. (1981) *Clinical use of acoustic impedance testing in audiological diagnoses*. In Beagley, H.A. (Ed.) *Audiology and Audiological Medicine*, Oxford. O.U.P.

Chapter 4

THE EXTENT OF THE HEARING LOSS

THE PURE TONE AUDIOGRAM AND HEARING FOR SPEECH

The relationship between the pure tone audiogram and hearing for speech has received the attention of a large number of workers. Carhart [2] gave hearing tests to 682 persons with various types of deafness and found that he was better able to predict the hearing loss for speech by averaging the hearing losses at 512, 1024 and 2048 Hz than from seven other methods of calculation from the pure tone audiogram. A more complicated method was evolved by Fletcher [57] based on a table of loudness which included the relative contributions especially to intelligibility of various frequency bands. He also gave a simplified method of calculation that consisted of averaging the two smallest losses for the three tones 512, 1000 and 2000 Hz. He considered this method almost as accurate as the first. Palva [114] evaluated the various methods of estimating hearing loss for speech from the pure tone audiogram and concluded that the method prepared by Carhart proved most reliable. This method of calculation seems fairly generally accepted in most countries at the present time.

Cawthorn and Harvey [28] believed that the correlation between the audiogram and hearing loss for speech was very close in conductive deafness, but that it was not so close for other types. There seems to be considerable agreement that what each patient will hear of speech can not be predicted accurately from the audiogram in sensorineural hearing impairment. Palva, [114] found that nerve deafened cases with average hearing losses between 20 and 40dB had speech discrimination losses that varied between 10 and 30 percent.

Harold, [67] too found wide discrepancies between children with similar audiograms who had widely dissimilar speech test results (See Chapter 7).

The *aetiology* (cause of deafness) in sensorineural deafened cases had some bearing on auditory discrimination according to Cawthorn and Harvey. [28] Harold [67] found that a group of twenty children whose deafness was due to measles heard rather better than did children whose deafness resulted from one of eight other causes, and that six children who had acquired a hearing loss as a result of cerebral palsy heard speech significantly worse than did those in the other eight groups.

Wax in the ear canal (Cerumen).
Bergon,[12] in 1984, found that 26% of a group medical practice of 8,000 patients required irrigation of their ear canals to remove impacted wax. It was found to be the most common ear problem (following suppurative otitis media). The highest incidence occurred in the younger patients of Bergon's practice. Such statistics indicate that parents and teachers of deaf children should remain alert to the possibility of fluctuations in the children's hearing. These may necessitate adjustments to hearing aid listening levels for the younger children and may help to explain variability in hearing for speech test results, and if the conductive deafness is of long standing, speech production can also be adversely affected.

Provided the ear drum was healthy and intact, the American Academy of Otolaryngology - Head and Neck Surgery in 1991, recommended that patients (and parents) might use over-the-counter toiletries to cope with impacted wax. Detailed treatment data are available to parents, teachers and audiologists in articles such as that of Roeser and Roland.[124]

Otosclerosis: Although this bony growth occurs in the middle ear mostly in adulthood, in some cases adolescent children do have a problem with it, and like wax in the canal, it can impose an additional loss of hearing - sometimes by completely immobilising the stapes. Otosclerosis is an inherited condition and the course of its development should be carefully monitored in children where there is a family history of its occurrence.

The shape of the audiogram is considered by many workers to be important in determining whether a subject will hear well or not. Huizing,[80] Wedenberg,[151] and others contended that flat audiograms (those with approximately equal losses for all frequencies) are better from this point of view than are those that possess a downward slope for the higher frequencies. Harold, (Ibid) however, found surprisingly little relationship between audiogram shape and hearing for speech.

The presence or absence of a phenomenon known as *loudness recruitment* in subjects has been found by various workers to have some effect on the extent to which they are able to hear speech. Where recruitment is present, a deaf person is able to hear loud sounds as loudly (or almost as loudly) as does a person with normal hearing. A considerable body of literature exists on the subject and is discussed later (See Chapter 8).

When to the above factors are added others such as intelligence, age, language, background, familiarity with the test situation, and the degree of rapport established between child and tester, as well as a few others, it is easy to understand how two children may have identical audiograms yet may obtain quite different scores on word list tests.

Hirsh,[72] in 1952, considered that the relationship between the pure tone threshold and speech discrimination ability, was "... one of the greatest points of ignorance in clinical audiology" (page 149). Forty-eight years later, it must be said that the situation is much the same as far as small pure tone differences are concerned. (Undoubtedly, of course, subjects with average pure tone losses of 60 dB may be expected to hear speech significantly better than those with 90 dB losses, but whether such children will hear speech better than those with 65 dB losses, one cannot accurately predict.)

Having said that, however, it *is* possible, with experience, to look at audiograms and make some useful general statements about what many children with similar losses, *have* been able to hear after they have been fitted with appropriate hearing aids.

Fig: 4.1

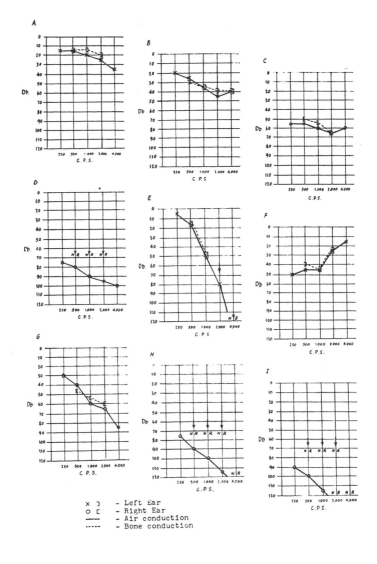

x ⅂ – Left Ear
o ⸦ – Right Ear
——— – Air conduction
----- – Bone conduction

Fig. 4:1 represents the better ear thresholds of nine hypothetical cases all of whom may be said to have sensorineural hearing losses. Before commenting briefly on these, it is stressed again that audiograms should never really be interpreted in isolation - pure tone and speech tests of hearing form the basis of clinical audiometry.

Audiogram A (Hearing loss 20 dB). This child is not sufficiently deaf to wear a hearing aid,* but does have an annoying little hearing loss. Other things being equal, such a child might be expected to be coping satisfactorily in an ordinary (regular) school while sitting in the front of the class. The teacher should know about his/her disability. In particular this will ensure that the child is not penalised for behaviour that may seem like lack of attention or disobedience but which in fact may well be the result of not having heard or of having heard imperfectly. It is unlikely that his/her speech will have been adversely affected by such a hearing loss.

Audiogram B (Hearing Loss 35 dB). A child whose hearing in the better ear is represented in Audiogram B has a significant hearing loss, but with a hearing aid in good acoustic conditions many such children are able to hear simple word list material with 100 percent accuracy. Unaided, this child could be expected to hear the vowels of conversational speech fairly adequately, but some of the consonants would be heard imperfectly and in some cases not at all. In consequence of this, if the loss is of long standing, and the child has not used a hearing aid regularly, his/her production of some consonants might well be defective. When watching the speaker, such children can sometimes understand running speech fairly well unaided.

The majority of children with hearing losses of this order seem to cope well in ordinary schools when hearing aids are worn properly. Many such children dislike having to wear hearing aids. "I can hear as well without it", they frequently say. They *do* need aids, however, and should be persuaded to wear them in school at least. These children should sit at the front of the class or near the teacher in open plan classrooms. Some require speech therapy to help them articulate consonants clearly.

Audiogram C (Hearing Loss 60 dB). This audiogram represents a more serious hearing loss. If listening unaided, a child with such an audiogram would hear very little of the sounds of ordinary conservational speech. The child's own speech will be grossly defective unless he/she has been given special help. Despite this, a flattish audiogram at about this level is regarded by many audiologists as a "good" one, since very often such cases hear well with amplification. It is common for such a case as this to obtain a score of 70 percent correct in a word list test when listening with his/her hearing aid and

---

* Hearing aids are not normally recommended unless the average hearing loss by air conduction in the better ear is at least 30 dB and this loss is irreversible.

without watching the speaker, providing the acoustic conditions are good. If such children are of reasonable intelligence and have a good home as well as an understanding teacher, many are able to manage in ordinary schoolrooms. They do, however, require special educational treatment involving, perhaps a weekly visit from a teacher of the deaf and 1 or 2 hours per day from a teacher's assistant. (See Appendix 1:1).

Audiogram D (Hearing Loss 88 dB). A child with this audiogram is severely deaf. Many such children hear a great deal of speech when it is amplified, and using a simplified word list test (as described above), some of these children are able to obtain scores of 40 and even 50 percent by listening alone.

Audiogram E (Hearing Loss 48 dB - Steeply sloping). Hearing losses of this type appear from time to time. This shape of audiogram is frequently found when a child has sustained anoxia at birth. Very often deafness is not suspected for a long time because such children are able to respond to very quiet sound provided it is of low frequency. They may hear a car or an airplane when it is a long way off simply because there is enough sound of low frequency to become audible to them. Similarly, the *fundamental frequency* of a speaker's voice will be audible to them, so that often when their name is called quite softly, they will turn in the direction of the speaker. Parents, teachers and doctors then frequently think, "Oh well, whatever else is wrong with young Billy, at least he's not deaf". Unfortunately their retarded speech development and their failure to establish normal relations with their peers often lead to diagnoses of "innate dullness", or perhaps of "brain damage", "aphasia" or "auditory imperception". In fact, such children are simply very deaf over most of the speech range of frequencies and, of course, for sounds above these.

Hearing aids are sometimes of little benefit to them - amplification of the lower frequencies makes those sounds unpleasantly loud, and the hearing mechanism is so defective for the higher frequencies, that intelligibility is rarely attainable. The majority of such children require special educational treatment in their local regular schools. (See Appendix 1:1 and Appendix 1:2). They then obtain a clear speech pattern to lipread and are able to be given constant help with their speech. They hear the melody of music very clearly but are not able to understand the words of songs - speech often being heard rather like a succession of "oo" sounds. Understandably, without recognition of the hearing problem, many such children can become insecure and withdrawn.

Audiogram F (Hearing Loss 38 dB). Very occasionally, a child is found to have better hearing for high frequencies than for low ones. Such children often hear speech well when it is aided, and consonants, not surprisingly, are heard particularly clearly. Unaided speech to such cases lacks body and this is sometimes reflected in their own speaking voices. An ear level hearing aid, an ordinary (regular) school placement and awareness of the child's difficulty are sometimes all that is required, but often help from a teacher's assistant is welcomed.

Audiogram G (Hearing Loss 102 dB). This is quite a common audiogram for sensorineural cases, i.e., hearing is frequently worse for high frequencies than for the lower ones. Voice quality is often quite good due to the fact that a useful amount of the vowel sounds can be heard when a hearing aid is used and pitch and rhythm are able to be perceived and incorporated into these childrens' speech. Treatment could include a weekly visit from a teacher of the deaf and that suggested above for Audiogram F children.

Audiogram H (Hearing Loss 102 dB). Although profoundly deaf, many children with audiograms such as this, show fair discrimination between known words or vowels when powerful hearing aids have been carefully fitted. Usually they are able to discriminate pitch and rhythm from music when it is amplified. Unless given a great deal of speech therapy by skilled teachers such children frequently develop speech that is not intelligible to untrained listeners. Children with such severe hearing losses should be considered for cochlear implanting - See Chapter 11.

Audiogram I (Hearing Loss 112 dB [Approximately]). Despite very little hearing for speech or any other sound, many cases are able to discriminate between some pairs of vowels when they are presented in random order. Van Uden and others have found that it is possible for even such deaf children as this to perceive music and derive pleasure from dancing and from listening to music (See Chapter 10).

Very few children are found to have less hearing than shown in Audiogram I but even children with this degree of hearing loss are able to attend their local ordinary schools provided great care is taken in preparing the schools and adequate support is arranged for them. (See Appendix 1:1 and 1:2.)

Profoundly deaf people without very successful cochlear implants, will never hear speech as clearly as those who are only partially hearing, no matter how loudly the speech is delivered. The ultimate limitation of hearing aids is not a physical, but a physiological one. In other words, the physicists can give a hearing aid any output and any frequency response which is asked for, but there are people whose organ of hearing is so defective that speech can never be made intelligible to them without implants (See Chapter 11).

There are, of course, an infinite number of categories of deafness - ranging from losses that are only just significant right through to those where sounds must be presented so loudly that they are almost painful before they can be detected.

The percentage of children who are totally deaf has been found to be very small.

The American Medical Association* drew up a table for converting audiometric dB losses into percentage of loss for speech. This table showed that they considered a patient with a threshold of 90 dB from 512 to 1024 Hz and of 95 dB from 1024 to 2048 Hz to have a "total loss of serviceable hearing". These levels were used in compensation cases, where through war injury or accident, or as a result of an illness such as meningitis or scarlet fever, a person had become profoundly deaf.

Ewing and Ewing[53] after outlining courses for children with differing hearing losses, suggested that for those whose impairments exceeded 95 dB, auditory training was likely to be of no benefit and that sight and touch should take the place of hearing.

Silverman as a result of his work on increasing tolerance levels (1947) suggested that some individuals who had previously been termed "totally deaf" might be reached by auditory stimulation through properly designed apparatus.

The workers who have studied most extensively the use of hearing aids by children whose hearing losses exceed 100 dB are van Uden and fellow workers at St. Michielsgestel Instituut voor Doven in Holland.[143][144] Although it would not be true to say that they believe every profoundly deaf child can benefit from the use of a hearing aid, they have certainly shown that the majority can and that every child should be given a lengthy trial.

My own experience with such deaf children tends to confirm van Uden's findings. If they can be enabled to hear even a trace of speech - and all but a handful can - then surely it can only be of benefit to them. Even if all the vowels they can hear sound rather like a muffled, "oo", the sound of voice must provide a link with the people who speak to them. How important it must be psychologically to a young deaf child, for example, in giving him or her that sense of belonging - the realisation that when his mother speaks, "sound" accompanies the movements of her lips. Van Uden[145] has quoted a girl whose hearing loss was 100 dB and who on removing her hearing aid said, "Now I am alone again". The Ewings have made the point, too, that even sound imperfectly heard can help a deaf person realise when words begin and end, as this is not always possibly by speech reading alone.

Further evidence of the value of sound to a profoundly deaf person is contained

---

* In the following discussion of hearing losses, the former American Standard losses have been brought nearer to the International Standard by deleting 10 dB, from hearing losses given.

in the following case study.

Mrs. M.....
Aged:	Thirty-two years
Aetiology:	Scarlet fever
Age at onset of deafness:	Two years
Hearing loss:	113 dB (approximately)
A skillful lipreader	
Speech:	Mostly intelligible but grossly defective

Mrs. M. was fitted with a hearing aid for the first time when thirty-two years of age. After a three-week introductory period consisting of five talks on hearing aids, how they should be worn and cared for, and what benefit might be expected when wearing one, Mrs. M. was issued with her aid. At the end of the first day she reported: "I have had a very interesting day. I heard my children talking for the first time. Their voices sounded high to me compared with Mrs. ... who lives nearby and who seems to have a gruff voice. I heard the cupboard doors click when I shut them, and oh! the noise of the dishes when I was washing up. I also heard the water splashing on the walls of the swimming baths when I was watching the children swimming this afternoon. Do car gears make a noise when you change them?!! (Emphasis author).

For the first two or three weeks Mrs. M. had considerable difficulty with headaches - often immediately after removing the aid. Sometimes wearing the aid made her dizzy, and she often woke with a headache. She found that a cup of tea often dispelled these. On one or two days during this early period Mrs. M. left the aid off completely. She was encouraged to *switch* it off rather than *take* it off when the sound became unpleasant.

Before the end of one month, Mrs. M. was wearing her aid continuously with no ill effects. During the five months under when she was observed, Mrs. M. reported hearing (imperfectly, of course) a variety of sounds, which included: doors shutting, furniture when moved on a hard floor, the vacuum cleaner, her own footsteps, shovelling coke, washing and drying dishes, the piano (sometimes), the dance band and a male soloist at a ball, laughter, children singing at a Girl Guide party, her children if they quarrelled in another room, an ambulance siren and people's voices. (Mrs. A. wrote "It was a wonderful thing to hear her friend's baby cry!" - With her own children and no hearing aid, she had only been able to see that they were crying.

Mrs. M. noted that "all people's voices are different". Some ladies' voices she said, were clear and high, some were soft and others were "active" (chatterboxes!). Men spoke with "firm" and "strong" voices. although being able to detect this pitch and quality in the voices, Mrs. M. was not able, or course, to obtain intelligibility. She felt however, that she was able to lipread better, and the neighbours all told her that her speech was more intelligible to them. I, personally, could perceive a slight, but not a striking, improvement in her speech. Mr. M. considered that a most valuable contribution which the hearing aid had made was that his wife had now become accustomed to keeping the level of her voice down, whereas previously he had frequently to remind her to do this.

A the end of the fifth month, Mrs. M. was asked if she thought the hearing aid worthwhile, and to this she replied. "Oh, yes, I wouldn't be without it. It has made life much more interesting for me."

Cases such as that cited above are very valuable ones, for three main reasons:

(a)   The majority of deaf people are not as deaf as this. It seems reasonable to assume, therefore, that having a less defective hearing organ, most of them should derive *more* benefit from sound than was the case here.

(b)   They emphasis that it is not essential to have a hearing aid during the first year or two of life to derive benefit from it. Older deaf children and adults (as well as some teachers and doctors) frequently use this as an argument for not obtaining hearing aids. Although it is desirable to begin early, it is never too late to make a start.

(c)   They emphasise to those of us who work with deaf children that hearing aid users *do* have problems, particularly those connected with physical discomfort in the early stages and teachers and parents of young children should watch closely for any signs of these.

Not all cases are as successful as that of Mrs. M., and as far as getting male old pupils of schools for the deaf to wear hearing aids is concerned, I have not had quite such good results to date. Factors involved in obtaining the full time use of aids are discussed in some detail in Chapter 10.

Conductive Hearing Losses: In addition to the sensorineural hearing impairment and its effect on children's reception of speech, it should also be remembered that children with hearing aids are just as likely as normally hearing ones to be troubled with *conductive* hearing impairments from time to time as a result of colds, middle ear infection and deposits of wax in the ear canal. When this *conductive* hearing impairment is added to the sensorineural loss the children can become significantly more impaired for a short time at least, until the conductive impairment of hearing is treated or clears itself up.

An excessive amount of impacted wax (cerumen), for example, has been shown to cause more and more severe hearing losses as it increased. With full occlusion of the ear canal, this loss was of 30 dB at 250 Hz, 45 dB at 1000 and 2000 Hz and 60 dB at 8000 Hz.

Provided the ear drum was healthy and intact, the American Academy of Otolaryngology - Head and Neck Surgery in 1991, recommended that patients (and parents) might use over-the-counter toiletries to cope with impacted wax.

The effect of impacted wax in the ear canal of a profoundly deaf child can, of course, be devastating audiologically. If, for example a child with a 90+ dB loss has a further 40 dB, added by impacted wax, the output of most hearing aids would not reach his or her threshold of audibility, let alone the best listening level.

Chapter 5

THE FREQUENCIES AND INTENSITIES
OF SPEECH SOUNDS

In speech training with hearing aids, one should really bear in mind: (a) the audiogram of the child; (b) the frequencies of the speech material and (c) the frequency characteristics and output of the hearing aid being used. The theory does not always work out exactly as it should in practice - children sometimes failing to hear sounds which they *should* be able to hear, and vice versa. The more one knows of the physics of speech, however, the more intelligently one is able to use hearing aids with deaf children and the more interesting does the work become.

The Production of Vowel Sounds

Fig. 5:1

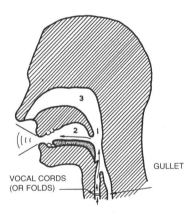

When the intercostal muscles contract, they pull the ribs outwards so that a vacuum is created within the cage or box-like structure of the chest. Air is thus sucked into the lungs and may be held there for quite a period if we desire it, simply by closing the little valve in the throat. This valve, located in the larynx and protected in the front by two pieces of cartilage which are popularly known as 'the Adam's apple', contains two folds in the wall of the larynx called the vocal folds - or more commonly, *vocal cords* (Fig. 5:1). When the vocal cords are drawn almost together, the air passing between them sets them in vibration, and a sound results. This sound is called the *fundamental* or *laryngeal tone*. The speed with which the vocal cords vibrate determines the pitch of the voice, and in any speaker (except some very deaf ones), the pitch rises and falls a great deal - as much as 100 Hz in a two-syllable word at times. The pitch of the fundamental ranges from about 90 Hz to 300 Hz. The average pitch of a woman's voice is about 250 Hz, roughly that of middle C on the piano. For men, the average fundamental tone is nearer 125 Hz. When only the edges of the cords are set in vibration, a very high pitched or "falsetto" voice results. When excess pressure is placed on the vocal cords, they are unable to vibrate freely throughout their whole length, and a hoarse, breathy type of speech is produced.

Laryngeal tones can be recorded by placing a microphone near the glottis. They sound rather like the indefinite sound such as a prolongation of the central vowel [ə] as in "fath<u>er</u>". Before the laryngeal tone reaches us it has passed through and been affected by the resonating chambers above, i.e., the oropharynx, the mouth and the nasal cavity (Fig. 5:1, 1, 2 and 3 respectively).

As the fundamental tone bounds about in these cavities, it causes them to resonate, before it issues from the lips as the sound we require. Just which frequencies emerge, depends largely upon the shape of the cavities and tension at that particular time. Little children (with normal hearing) soon learn to modify the shape of their mouths so that the vowel that issues forth sounds like the one they want to hear. Babies can frequently be heard experimenting with their voices in this way.

One does not teach speech to very deaf children for long before one realises that the tongue position is all important in obtaining clear vowels and diphthongs. In the diphthong [ai] (as in "tie"), for example, the tongue must be down at the back to give the [a] sound (as in "art") and must then move quickly forward and upward to the [I] position (as in "see") (Fig. 5:2, Positions 1 and 2). It is important to realise that whilst the resonator changes shape and thus alters the sound that comes from the speaker, the fundamental remains the same sound. If,

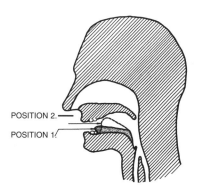

POSITION 2.

POSITION 1

Fig. 5:2

however, a scale is sung using one vowel sound - then the reverse applies. There is no change in the shape of the resonator so that the sound remains the same right up the scale, but the pitch is changing with each note and this is brought about by a tightening of the vocal cords and a gradual closing of the *glottis* (the gap between the cords).

It is possible to analyse each of the speech sounds and determine which frequencies comprise them and how much of each frequency is required to produce a particular sound. Harvey Fletcher[58], in his classic textbook of 1929, drew attention to this and analysed many of the phonemes. Fig. 5:3 represents three vowels that have been analysed to show the frequencies that make up these sounds.

Fig. 5:3

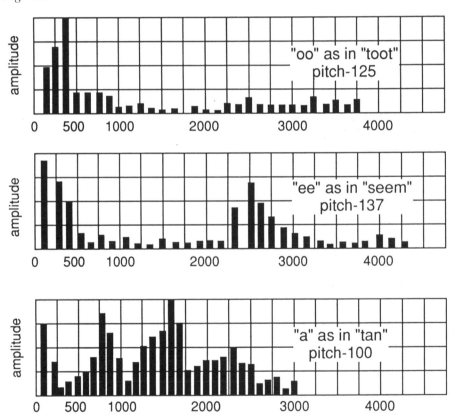

It is seen from these graphs that [u] as in "sh*oe*" is comprised mainly of low frequency sounds round about the 500 Hz level. The [I] in "sh*ee*p" has a band of pressure at the lower end of the scale, and then a second concentration of sound round about the 2,500 to 3,000 Hz level, and these two bands give this sound its particular quality.

A useful display of the analysis of first and second formants of English vowel sounds (spoken with an American accent), was shown in the 1979 edition of Davis[40]. A slightly adapted form of this is shown below in Fig. 5:4. By placing a blank sheet of paper across the upper frequencies of this figure at, say 1,000 Hz, one is helped to appreciate how limited auditory information is for children with little or no hearing for the higher frequencies. If the paper is moved still lower, to 800 Hz, it is possible to see that auditory discrimination between vowels is even more difficult and one realises that the second formants give each sound its particular quality to those with normal hearing. It also explains why children with little hearing above 1,000 Hz have extreme difficulty in discriminating between the [u] and [I] sounds, often complaining that the sounds are "the same". To them, of course, they *are* because their lower frequency components are almost identical and the second formant of [I] is out of their range of hearing.

In Fig. 5:4, the analyses of 12 vowels and 2 diphthongs show the first formants of the sounds remain fairly flat (between 100 and 400 Hz) while the second formants rise steadily from about 600 Hz to 2,400 Hz as the tongue moves forward and upwards towards the hard palate and the top teeth of the speaker. The tightening of the cheek and lip muscles as the tip of the tongue moves near the upper teeth, also helps to give the last 5 sounds in this list the larger proportion of high frequencies that are required to produce these phonemes.

Teachers of deaf children, speech therapists and audiologists have frequently found it helpful to learn the simple sentence "Who would know ought of art must work and then take his ease"* included in Fig. 5:4 to enable them to recall the order in which the phonemes occur from the back of the mouth to the front and whether the tongue should be up or down at the front or back or in the middle when saying each sound.

It is certainly helpful to teachers when they are trying to assist deaf children to produce more accurate vowels and diphthongs and the children are not able to monitor their speech through aided hearing. These children are really "flying blind" (to use an aviator's terminology), and must rely on the expression on their teacher's face to indicate whether they are well away from the sound required, are getting nearer to it, or finally, (with a happy smile of encouragement), "Yes! That is it!". "Now just say it once or twice more" (to help the child remember next time or perhaps (if it seems well established), when he/she gets home, or to the hostel, that afternoon.

---

* If a slightly 'Italian' accent is used, the neutral vowel [ə] will also be included - "must [ə] work"

Fig. 5:4

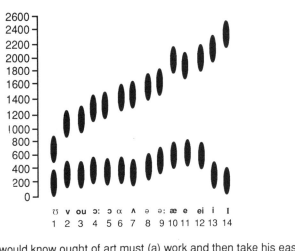

ʊ v ou ɔ: ɔ ɑ ʌ ə ə: æ e ei i ɪ
1 2 3   4   5 6 7 8 9 10 11 12 13 14

Who would know ought of art must (a) work and then take his ease
1   2   3   4 5 6   7   8   9   10   11   12 13   14

Teachers and speech therapists often ask a child first to say a clear [I] sound and next to repeat after them, "tee, tee, tee, tee, tee". If this is repeated quite rapidly, the tip of the child's tongue remains very near the position it should be in when the [I] sound is produced. (If children have difficulty in saying [t] properly, it is often possible to ask them to say "thee, thee, thee, thee" which is a relatively simple syllable to say and yet the tongue is again in the region required to say [I] and one can gradually introduce the more difficult [t] sound later.) *See Endnotes p89.

To say [ə] as in "work", (No. 9 sound), the blade of the tongue is raised in the centre of the mouth. For sounds 9-14, the tip of the tongue moves to 5 different positions. From the open [ə:] sound to the closed [i:]. (The lips and cheeks also tighten as these sounds are produced and the air stream is directed up to the hard palate and the teeth which also add to the creation of the high frequency sounds needed to produce the second formants.)

The Production of Consonants
Consonants are produced when an obstruction occurs in the flow of the breath stream.

Classification

(a)   Consonants are classified into two types according to whether they are voiced or unvoiced, e.g., "p" and "b", "s" and "z", "k" and "g", etc.

(b) They may be further classified by considering "where" the obstruction occurs to the breath stream, e.g., the consonant "p" occurs when both lips block the airstream and the sound is in consequence known as a "bilabial".

(c) A third method of classification is derived by noting "the nature" of the obstruction. In "k", for example, air pressure is built up at the back of the mouth, and then suddenly released with a little explosion - all such consonants, e.g., p, b, t, d, k, g are known as *plosives*. Others are caused by the friction of air passing through a narrow gap, e.g., f and v, [θ] and [∂], [ʃ] and [z] etc., and are known as *fricatives*.

Using the above three methods of classification we may thus describe consonants as follows: "b" is a voiced, bilabial, plosive consonant; "[θ] is an unvoiced, palato-dental, fricative, etc.

It may be seen from Table 5:1 that the unvoiced consonants in running speech have no really low frequency components - all beginning at about 1500 Hz or higher, and that all consonants voiced and unvoiced, have important high frequencies that are critical to their intelligibility.

Table 5:1

FREQUENCIES OF CONSONANTS

Sound						
θ						About 6000
o	250–300					4500 – 6000
∂						
s						5000 – 6000
z	200 –300				4000 – 5000	
f					4500 – 5000	
v	300 – 400				3500 – 4500	
t				2500 – 3500		
d	300 – 400			2500 – 3000		
k	300 – 400			2000 – 2500		
g	200 – 300			2000 – 3000		
l	250 – 400			2000 – 3000		
p			1500 –	2000		
b	300 – 400			2000 – 3000		
h			1500 – 2000			
sh			1500 – 2000		4500 – 5500	
ch			1500 – 2000		4000 – 5000	
j	200 – 300			2000 – 3000		
m	250 – 350	1000 – 1500		2500 – 3500		
n	250 – 350	1000 – 1500		2500–3000		
ng	250 – 400	1000 – 1500		2000 – 3000		
r	600 – 800	1000 – 1500		2000 – 2400		

Adapted from Harvey Fletcher (1929): *Speech and Hearing*. van Nostrand. (Sounds analysed during quiet conversational speech.)

It should be remembered that there is a very important difference in the frequency spectrum of consonants that are said in normal running speech and those that are said in isolation and emphasised (as is often the case in speech teaching). There is a distinct lowering of the frequency components in fricatives when forced, and in plosives, many become like "white noise", i.e., a multi-frequency sound, all appearing to be very much the same - rather like the indefinite "breathy" sound that results when someone blows across a microphone in a hall to test the amplifying system.

Children who are very deaf may be enabled to hear the sound of consonants, but the majority can never hope to hear them intelligibly nor to discriminate among them, unless, of course, as suggested earlier, a cochlear implant operation has been successfully completed. (See Chapter 11), It is of tremendous importance, as indicated above, in speech teaching with such children, for the teacher to show by his or facial expression when the child is saying the sound incorrectly, nearly correctly, and finally correctly. Remember, too, that encouragement rather than coercion is essential when helping deaf children to speak more intelligibly.

THE SONAGRAPH

Analysing the frequency components of speech is not an easy matter because the range of frequencies is so complex and each syllable is so fleeting. SonaGraph instruments have provided a very satisfactory means of analysing a short sample of speech material. Other sounds can, of course, by analysed with them; bird songs, animal noises, the sound stimuli which are used in tests of hearing for very young children, etc.

Fig. 5:5

The *SonaGraph* (Fig. 5:5), analyses any sound signal as a function of both tine and frequency. The resultant portrayal, known as a *sonagram*, displays frequency along the vertical axis, time along the horizontal axis and intensity by the darkness of the display (fig. 5:6). Frequency is shown up to 8,000 Hz in a vertical distance of four inches or 10cm (those included here have been reduced in size). The sonagram covers a period of time equivalent to 2.4 seconds for a horizontal distance of approximately 12.5 inches (31.5cm).

In operation, the wanted signal, e.g., a phrase, is first recorded on a magnetic disc. It is played back over and over again. On each repetition, the signal is scanned by a 45 Hz band-pass filter, i.e., the first filter lets through a narrow band of frequencies - say from 500-545 Hz to begin with. At each repetition the filter is effectively shifted in frequency, e.g., from 500-545 to 505-550 and then from 510-555, etc.

The output of the analysing filter is then recorded on dry facsimile paper (Fig. 5:6) that is fastened around a rotating drum. The recording stylus shifts gradually up the frequency scale in step with the scanning oscillator.

Fig. 5:6

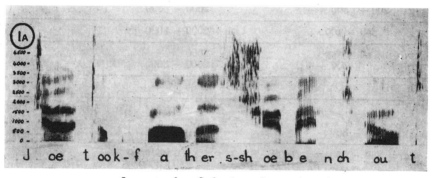

	Joe	took	father's	shoe	bench	out
Hz	150	140	145	180	110	110

Variations in the pitch of vowel sounds in conversational speech

Consider briefly the sample of speech, "Joe took father's shoe bench out," as portrayed in Fig. 5:6. This (quaint) phrase is one that has been used in the Bell Telephone Laboratories for many years because it contains a variety of sounds that are strategically placed for analysing purposes.

The [dʃ] in "Joe" is seen here to be of short duration and mostly of frequencies above 2,000 Hz. The diphthong [ou] was comprised of four *formants* - dark bands representing the frequencies where the sound had greatest energy. The [t] of "took" and of "out" are short and, although as Fletcher suggests in Table 5:2, most of the energy is between 2,500 and 3,500 Hz, a certain amount of the plosive contains lower frequencies. This is possibly due to a slight degree of forcing as this sound was said close to the microphone. The [ʊ] sound in "took" is seen to be very short in duration, a fact not always appreciated by teachers of the deaf, and the k, f, b, and h, as said here, were scarcely audible - all these consonants acting rather as complete blocks to the air stream rather than displaying their distinctive frequencies as when said in isolation. [z] and [ʃ] are interesting - due to some forcing, both sounds are rather lower in frequency than one would expect (Table 5:1), but each is clearly defined and the [z] is seen to glide into the lower frequency [ʃ] sound. The second and third formants of [ɛ] in "bench" can be seen to be bending upwards as the mouth opens from the plosive [b].

It is possible by counting the number of the vertical striations in the phonemes to calculate the frequency of the *fundamental* or *laryngeal* tone of each. This has been done for six of the seven vowels displayed in Fig. 5:6.

It is interesting that the stressed syllable ("sh*oe*") should be so much higher in pitch than the other sounds. Changes in pitch between vowels of up to 100 Hz are not uncommon, and frequently rises occur for emphasis and, of course, when shouting.

Vowel formants are labelled F_1, F_2, F_3, etc. in the order in which they occur in the frequency scale. The fundamental voice frequency is labelled F_0. The first formant (F_1) is usually the strongest. There are always two formants and often a third, associated with each vowel (Fig. 5:6).

Although formants can be counted up to 10!, the relative importance of the formants of voiced sounds decrease above F_2. Formant 3 and F_4 contribute to speakers' accents in certain vowel sounds and with F_0, account for speaker differences but F_1 and F_2 govern the essential character of each sound.

The fact that some of the frequency components of vowel sounds analysed here vary quite considerably from Harvey Fletcher's published data may be caused to some extent by the fact that he refers to American speakers whereas the accent recorded here is a New Zealand one (slightly harsh and somewhat strident!).

INTENSITIES OF SPEECH SOUNDS

Not all speech sounds are of the same strength. The sounds [ɔ], [ʌ],[ou], [ai] and [au], for example are about 20 dB more intense than p or b or d. In Table 5:2, the relative strengths of all the sounds are given when used in conversational speech and these are graphed in Fig. 5:7.

The mean intensity of the twelve vowels and diphthongs measured above is 56.90 dB. It is not suggested that teachers, speech therapists or audiologists should learn Table 5:2 by heart: (a) because the list is incomplete; (b) because the differences in the intensity of so many of the sounds is so very slight, and (c) because the order of ranking as given here is very frequently upset by the use of *accent* or *emphasis*, and by speech differences. Fletcher[57] states that "syllabic power varies more with the emphasis given than with the vowel used. A vowel in an accented syllable has three or four times as much phonetic power as one in an unaccented syllable".

Fig. 5:7

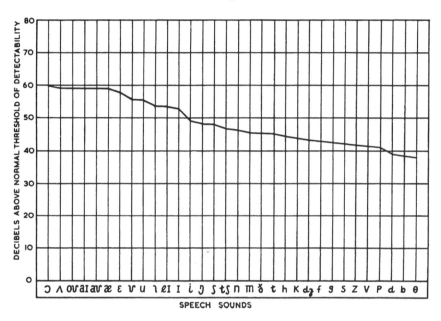

Intensities of Speech Sounds

Table 5:2

ɔ	for	60 db	n		46.8
ʌ	cup	59.6	m		45.4 dB
oʊ	home	59.6	ð	the	44.2
aɪ	mine	59.5	t		44.1
aʊ	cow	59.2	h		43.9
æ	cat	59.2	k		43.8
ɛ	ten	58.4	dʒ	jump	43.7
ʊ	took	55.9	f		43.6
u	school	55.9	g		42.9
l	let	53.5	s		42.4
eɪ	play	53.5	z		41.6
ɪ	bit	52.6	v		41.4
i	team	49.4	p		40.6
ŋ	ring	48.9	d		38.9
ʃ	shop	48.9	b		38.8
tʃ	chop	47.2	θ	thin	38.7

Fig. 5:8

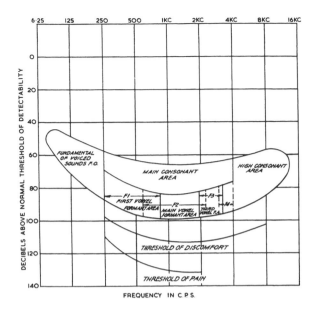

The Ewings[51] gave as an example of this: "This is a very short corridor", saying that the intensity of the vowel in "sho*rt*" would be three or four times greater than that in "corrid*or*". They went on to agree with Fletcher that trained speakers probably stressed the weaker sounds of speech rather more than did those who were untrained, and suggested that where such emphasis was given, the speech was better heard by those with defective hearing.

In view of the above variables, if one remembers that very often consonants are roughly 10 or 15 dB weaker than vowels and diphthongs, and that a stressed syllable is 3 or 4 times stronger than the same syllable when it is unstressed, it is as much as most workers need to know regarding the intensities of phonemes.

Information about frequencies and intensities of speech sounds, which were analysed by Fant[54], has been summarised in graph form by Wedenberg (Fig. 5:8). The latter's scheme of auditory training has been briefly referred to on pages 202-3.

Very useful "*speech envelopes*" have been produced by Erber[48], which help deaf children appreciate that their speech must be much more rapid if they hope to attain more normal speech production (See Fig. 5:9). In their effort to obtain near normal production of individual phonemes, it is natural that they will produce a more laboured form of speech. If asked to match the near normal rate, however, definition of consonants, particularly, is lost. Slower speech can also, of course, become rather tedious for the listener.

An effort must be made to speed up the children's speech but also retain as much intelligibility of essential elements as possible. Ling, in his text book. *Speech and Hearing Impaired Child* gives much attention to these two aspects of speech production in his 7 stage teaching strategy.[97]

Fig. 5:9

"The United States of America"

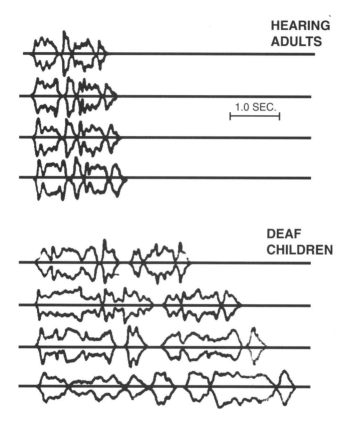

Endnotes

N.B. Speech material should be written in home-school notebooks *only* when it is *really well established*. Otherwise children try to practice errors and their parents (and grandparents) can become confused and disappointed. When definite speech improvement is achieved however, details should be sent immediately to parents and hostel parents. In this way, they can become interested in each child's success and are able to give invaluable assistance by reminding the child to use that aspect of speech improvement at regular intervals during succeeding weeks.

* Parents and hostel "parents", too, should let teachers and speech therapists know of any successes *they* have noticed in a child's speech or of particular difficulties that they wish a child might overcome. In this way the collaborative work between professionals and families can be maintained. (Parents are often deterred from trying to teach speech to their children although of course they frequently wish that they could do more to help them attain intelligibilitiy). It has traditionally been felt that the happy relationship which should exist between a parent and child can be threatened if parents try continually to correct defective speech. It is generally felt best for parents to commend good speech whenever it occurs rather than continually to monitor faults.

Chapter 6

SPEAKER DIFFERENCES AND ACOUSTIC CONDITIONS

Beranek (1954) has quoted Egan (1948), who showed that different speakers were heard with varying degrees of intelligibility by adult listeners with normal auditory acuity. Four radio announcers read PB* words in quiet and noisy conditions. In quiet, the most intelligible speaker obtained 95 percent of correct word articulation and the least intelligible, 90 per cent. Egan found that differences in intelligibility between speakers were much more significant in noise; the most intelligible was 70 per cent but the least only 45 per cent.

Nearly all hearing aid users comment upon the differences in intelligibility of the voices of various speakers. Some believe they hear male voices better than female ones, others that people who use a rapid or "staccato" type of delivery are difficult to hear through a hearing aid, and all seem to agree that there is a breathy or "catarrhal" type of voice which is particularly difficult to hear.

It has been possible to show that very significant differences do exist in the intelligibility of the speech of several speakers for children with sensorineural deafnesses who were wearing hearing aids (Dale[36]). A group of ten speakers recorded one list each of the adapted M/J word list test (Appendix 2:2). The speakers were eight teachers of the deaf who had been selected at random (except that four were men and four were women), and one male and one female graduate. Twenty children were divided evenly into two groups and each listened to five speakers. The scores obtained by the two groups showed that differences did indeed exist in the intelligibility of the ten speakers.

In Group 1 the speaker who was most intelligible scored 68 per cent correct, whilst the least intelligible speaker scored only 43.5 per cent. In Group 2, the best and worst mean scores were 72.3 per cent and 48.0 per cent, respectively. Twenty "t" tests were made between mean scores obtained for each two speakers, and in eleven cases the differences were found to be significant at the one per cent level of confidence. In three other cases, differences were significant at the 5 per cent level.

If one teacher's speech (without being lipread) is much less intelligible than anothers (as is the case with the extremes quoted above), this could be a sufficiently important factor to be given consideration in the selection and training of teachers of deaf children.

---

* Phonetically Balanced

The question also arises as to whether less intelligible speech is remediable. It was noted, for example, that the two speakers who were heard least well had very poor breath control. Neither was in the habit of breathing deeply and one stated that she had "never been able to shout properly". Both voices lacked resonance and this showed up very clearly when sonagrams were made of them.

Fig. 6:1 represents recordings of the speakers who were heard best in each group and those who were heard least well. Sonagram A is that of the male speaker whose speech was most intelligible. Vowels and consonants are nearly all clearly defined. The third and fourth vowel formants are clear, and the vertical striations show the voice to be deep in pitch and well modulated. [ou] = 150 Hz, [u] = 180 Hz and [ɛ] = 100 Hz. Sonagram B is that of the female speaker who was most intelligible. Prior to her training as a teacher of the deaf, this person had been a BBC announcer. Again all the vowel formants except the [u] of "sh*oe* bench' are strongly portrayed and the consonants are very well defined. There is perhaps a little more *fill* between the formants than is the case in A. The laryngeal tone or pitch of the voice was rather low in frequency and the voice well modulated [ou] = 220 Hz, [u] = 290 Hz and [ɛ] = 190 Hz.

Fig. 6:1

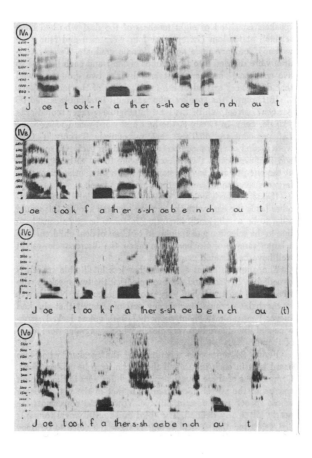

Sonagrams C and D, however, portray extremely poor vowel formants in nearly every instance. Those that are particularly defective are the neutral vowel [ə] in "fath*er*", and the long [u] of "sh*oe* bench". None of the vowels or diphthongs is rich in harmonics with the exception of [ou] in "Joe" in Sonogram D and here the formants lack definition. The consonants are fairly clear, though not possessing the precision of those of the male speaker.

Further research is required to ascertain more clearly the reason for the intelligibility and the causes of the unintelligibility of various voices.

ACOUSTIC CONDITIONS

Acoustics. Not a great deal has been written about the importance of acoustic conditions to hearing aid users, yet it is fairly easy to illustrate that the type of listening conditions that prevail in a room can be critical to the successful use of a hearing aid. Not nearly enough attention has been paid in the past to the acoustics of classrooms for normally hearing children, let alone those for deaf and partially hearing ones. J.E.J. John and H. Thomas[89] have made very practical suggestions for the siting and construction of buildings that are to be used by children wearing aids. Two aspects of acoustic conditions concern the hearing aid user, noise and reverberation.

Noise
Harold[67] showed:

(a)   that hearing for speech was adversely affected by noise, but that it did not alter the level of intensity at which optimum hearing took place. This may explain why so many hearing aid users rarely adjust their hearing aid volume controls in different acoustic conditions.

(b)   that sensorineurally deafened cases heard speech much less well in noise than did subjects with conductive deafness. It is thus of considerable importance to reduce noise levels in schools and classes for deaf children, since all but a handful of such children possess deafness which is sensorineural in origin.

It is best to eliminate noise at its source rather than try to exclude it once it is produced.

External noise, from traffic or from industry, can create impossible listening conditions - noise levels up to 100-120 dB. Careful siting of school buildings is therefore most essential.

"If the use of a site with a noise level of greater than 70 dB is unavoidable, extensive and expensive insulation is necessary", John & Thomas[89].

Trees, evergreen hedges, artificial embankments, and the erection of other buildings between the source of the noise and the classrooms, all improve listening conditions. Double glazing is another very effective means of excluding noise from rooms, but it is then usually necessary to install ventilators that can be both costly and noisy.

There is not a great deal that class teachers can do about controlling external noise - except, of course, to keep on complaining if it is really bad.

Internal noise, from corridor and stair traffic, from toilets, and from adjoining classrooms. Four inch brick walls, discontinuous flooring, and floor coverings of rubber or some such resilient material have all been helpful in reducing noises created within the building but outside the classroom.

Room noise from moving of furniture, shuffling of feet, turning pages, opening and closing drawers, artificial ventilation systems, etc. Children can be trained to be reasonably quiet in their movements about a room and when shifting tables or chairs. The use of rubber pads on chair and table legs is well worthwhile. Sheet rubber over foam rubber is probably the best type of floor covering, but other substitutes are available that seem almost as effective and durable and that are much less expensive. A well-covered floor is a tremendous help in reducing room noise.

It is often recommended that for ordinary children, classroom noise should not exceed 35-40 dB above 20µPa. The Ministry of Education suggested that 25-30 phons was permissible in classrooms for ordinary children.

John[†] regarded 25-30 phons as the minimum requirement in schools for the deaf.

Reverberation

The term *reverberation* is roughly synonymous with *echo*. When a person speaks in a room, the sound of the voice travels out (in compressions and rarefactions), at a speed of 1,100 feet per second. On striking an object such as a wall or floor or ceiling, the sound is deflected and carries on to the next obstruction, where it is deflected again, and so on. If the surface of the obstruction met is hard and shiny, the sound rebounds with little loss of energy (Fig. 6:2). Tiled bathrooms, for example, are very reverberant places.

[†]Discussion with Mr. J.E.J. John

Fig. 6:2

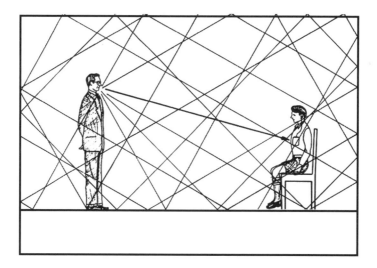

If the surface is soft or has been covered with good quality sound absorbent lagging material, then the sound enters the material (acoustic tiles, carpets, soft furnishings, etc.) and much of its energy is dissipated by generating heat or by causing movements of the surfaces. In Fig. 6:3, the sound is seen to be "killed" at the walls, floor and ceiling, and in consequence there is much less distortion of the sounds created in the room.

The diagrams are very much simplified just to emphasise the effect of acoustic treatment. In fact, even in a well-treated classroom, a sound of 60 dB would bounce from wall to wall twenty or thirty times before it became inaudible.

Fig. 6:3

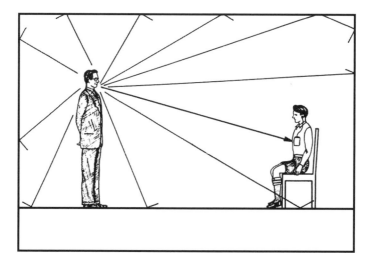

John[‡] reported the results of experiments that showed the effect of speaking at various distances from a microphone on the speech reception scores of normal listeners. Word lists were recorded on magnetic tape at distances of three inches, six inches, eighteen inches, three feet and nine feet. When delivered through a group hearing aid at a level of 65 dB above detectability, the articulation scores obtained were 96 per cent, 94 per cent, 80 per cent, 72 per cent, and 65 per cent respectively. The reverberation time existing in the room in which the tests were made approximated that of the "traditional type of classroom", and John concluded that reverberation could seriously limit the value of hearing aids for children. He maintained that, due to wide differences from room to room, it was difficult to lay down acoustic standards that could be universally applied. he suggested, however, that for small classrooms, as were commonly found in schools for the deaf, satisfactory results could be obtained if a quarter of the surface was treated with good quality absorbent materials. Usually, if the ceiling and about the top one to one and a half metres of the walls are covered, the treatment is quite effective.

It was thought advisable to compare the scores obtained by children wearing hearing aids in the poor acoustic conditions existing in some classrooms with those obtained when they were tested in the good acoustic conditions of an audiology clinic. The group consisted of twelve children aged between ten and fifteen years whose mean I.Q. was 106.00 (S.D. 20.6). All were attending ordinary (regular) schools. The tests were made at various distances from the microphone. The opportunity was also taken to ascertain how suitable listening conditions were in these classrooms for children with normal hearing.

In the classrooms, before each test began, the partially hearing child was asked to sit in the front row directly in front of the speaker. All the class were given sheets of paper on which three columns of numbers had been set out. The following instructions were given: "I am going to say some words and I want you to write down what I say. They are quite simple words like "house", "boat", "dog", and so on. If you don't hear a word clearly, write what you think it was or put a dash. Don't worry if you don't hear a word properly, and don't try to find out what it was from anyone sitting near you. Do you understand what to do?" An M/J word list was then delivered that was monitored at 70 dB with a sound level meter (See p.53 Fig. 2:10), eighteen inches from the speaker. Each word was preceded by the carrier phrase, "Number ... is". This served the dual purpose of building up reverberation in the room and ensuring that the children did not lose the place in the list. At the completion of the first list, the partially hearing child was moved to a position about half way down the classroom (at twelve to sixteen feet from the speaker, 4-5 metres), and the next list was read. The partially hearing child then sat on the back row twenty to twenty-four feet from the speaker, (6-7 metres), and the last list was read.

[‡]During lectures at Manchester University

Similar tests were made again with the hearing impaired children in a clinic which had been well treated acoustically. On this occasion the M/J lists were delivered at twelve inches, four feet and twenty-two feet from the microphone.

Table 6:1 illustrates the detrimental effect on intelligibility that results from varying the distance of the speaker from the microphone in very reverberant and slightly reverberant conditions.

Table 6.1

ARTICULATION SCORES OBTAINED IN DIFFERENT ACOUSTIC CONDITIONS BY TWELVE PARTIALLY HEARING CHILDREN

Distance from microphone	12"	4'	14'	22'
Good listening conditions	84%	70.8%		64%
Poor listening conditions		54.4%	44.8%	39.2%

The table emphasises the finding of John (above) with normally hearing subjects that the drop in intelligibility is most marked in the first few feet as one moves away from the microphone, e.g., in the good conditions there was a drop in intelligibility of about 13 per cent in the first three feet, but of only 7 per cent in the next eighteen feet. The importance of speaking close to the microphone is clearly illustrated. It will be shown later that this is not always practical to arrange in some classroom situations, but teachers and others should realise the value of speaking close to the microphone whenever it is possible to do so.

Fig. 6:4

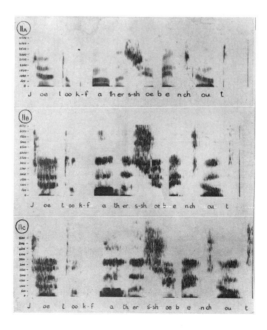

The decrease in intelligibility is also much more rapid in poor acoustic conditions than is the case in quiet and non-reverberant ones.It is possible to illustrate the effect on speech induced by varying distances from a microphone in good and in poor acoustic conditions by means of sonagrams (Figs. 6:4 and 6:5). The sentence, "Joe took father's shoe bench out," has been recorded direct on to the Sonagraph recorder at twelve inches, six feet, and fifteen feet from the microphone in good and in poor acoustic conditions. The recordings in the non-reverberant conditions were made in the clinic in which the children had been tested (reverberation time <1 second). The input to the microphone was maintained at 70 dB for all recordings by monitoring with a sound level meter.

The wide band filter was used when the sonagrams were run off.

Fig. 6:4, Sonagram A (twelve inches in good acoustic conditions) shows a distinct record with frequency formants for the vowels clearly defined.

Sonagram B (six feet in good acoustic conditions), both vowels and consonants

Fig. 6:5

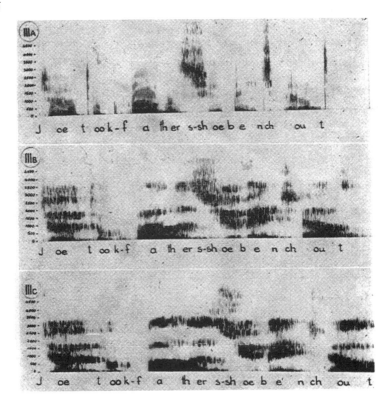

have lost a considerable degree of definition (see particularly [u] in "sh*oe* bench"), and the formants appear somewhat "smudgy". Due to the reverberation, the vowels have lengthened slightly and are beginning to "overrun" or mask the consonants (cf., [a] in "f$\underline{a}$ther's").

When speaking fifteen feet from the microphone a further deterioration in the clarity of all sounds is perceptible, with formants tending to merge one into another (cf., second and third formants of [ɛ] in "bench"). The gap that represented [ə] in "father" is seen to have closed considerably, but those for the sounds [k, f, b, and n] are still present although somewhat reduced.

Under reverberant acoustic conditions, distance from the microphone can be seen to be of critical importance to intelligible speech reception (Fig. 6:5). At twelve inches from the microphone (Fig. 6:5, Sonogram A), the pattern is relatively clear, although not as distinct as in the non-reverberant room at the same distance. At six feet and fifteen feet, however, reverberation is seen to produce marked perseverations in the vowel formants that *mutilate* the form of the succeeding consonants. When the sonograms of Figs: 6:4 and 6:5 are studied, it is not surprising that articulation scores obtained under these conditions differ by almost 50 per cent.

Endnotes

*   The mean hearing loss of Group 1 was 63.25 dB and of Group 2, 67.42 dB.

†   In Educational Guidance and the Deaf Child (Ed) AWG Ewing (1957), pp. 160-175.

‡   As indicated in Appendices 1-1 and 1-2, in many areas, over 80 per cent of children wearing hearing aids are now able to attend ordinary schools. To overcome the deleterious effect of noise and reverberation, the use of radio and infra -red waves has been found of great assistance as suggested in Chapter 1.

Chapter 7

BEST LISTENING LEVELS

Just how loud speech must be made to give each hearing impaired person the best possible listening experience has concerned a large number of workers in audiology. It is necessary, however, first to consider very briefly the method by which optimum levels are obtained.

THE ARTICULATION FUNCTION

(a)   *The Articulation Score*. When a list of words is read to a subject, the number of words heard correctly is known as his/her *articulation score*. Thus, if twenty-five words were heard correctly out of fifty, the subject has an articulation score of twenty-five (or of fifty per cent).

(b)   *The Articulation Curve*. Word lists may be presented quietly or loudly. When they are delivered at various levels of loudness to a subject, it is possible to plot a graph of the scores obtained (Fig. 7:1). This graph is called an *articulation curve*. Audiometry, according to Carhart[22] was based on the concept of the articulation function, i.e., the relationship between the percentage of speech items heard correctly by the subject and the intensity at which the items were delivered.
(The word *articulation* is derived from testing the fidelity of telephone communication systems - workers need to know how closely the speech sounds received by the listener "articulated" with those presented by the speaker in the other room, or building or city. Articulation score as used in the remainder of this section has nothing at all to do with a person's ability to say sounds correctly.) As can be seen in Fig. 7:1, articulation curves may vary a great deal in shape from one subject to another.

Factors that affect the shape of the curve have been considered by various writers to include: the deafness of the subject; the type of speech material used; the intelligence, education and interests of the subject; the type of amplifying equipment used,; the voice of the speaker (Fletcher[57]) and the aetiology of the deafness.[40] For pure conductive deafness, the shape of the curve remains the same as for normally hearing subjects (Fig. 7:1 - A), but is displaced to the right, that is to say, the most difficult words are heard correctly if they are presented loudly enough (Fig. 7:1 - B).

For subjects with severe sensorineural hearing losses, however, most writers agree that no matter what level of amplification is used, 100 per cent intelligibility is seldom attained[57]. (Fig. 7:1 - C and D). Since the advent of cochlear implanting, such statements have become less valid (See Chapter 11).

Fig. 7:1

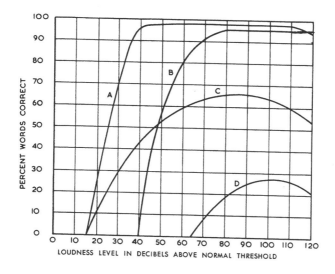

OPTIMUM LISTENING LEVELS

When subjects have normal hearing, the articulation curve has been found to flatten at an average of 35dB above detectability, i.e., subjects attain maximum intelligibility at that level (Egan[40]). From the following literature, it may be seen that this factor tended to dominate the thinking of workers in ascertaining best listening levels.

Lidén suggested that if the articulation curves for patients with various types of hearing losses did not diverge unduly from the normal, it should be possible to determine optimum levels for setting amplifying apparatus by simply adding 35 dB to their thresholds of detectability. In practice he found that in many cases such predictions could be inaccurate. Lidén also drew attention to the fact that where the hearing loss was pronounced, the level of uncomfortable loudness became a limiting factor to any such fixed increment of amplification, e.g., if a person's hearing loss was 100 dB, 135 dB of output might well be much too loud for him. In his study of 104 patients, sixty of whom had auditory impairments which were conductive in origin, Lidén gave consideration to the relationship between the level at which maximum score on word lists occurred and the level of most comfortable loudness of the subjects. In some cases, the latter were found to be only 20 dB above the patients' thresholds of detectability.

He concluded that comfort levels were not necessarily a valid criterion for obtaining optimum amplification levels.

In the Centre for Audiology and Education of the Deaf at Manchester University, for many years, the procedure for obtaining the correct listening level with children unable to co-operate in speech tests was: a) to find the child's threshold of detectability for voice, and (b) to add 30 dB to this (if it were practical to do so).

While investigating volume control adjustment in connection with hearing aid selection, Carhart[24] made a study of the reliability of the comfort level method of setting hearing aid gain controls. Using 413 partially deaf subjects, he found that the test-retest reliability of this method was high (r = .87).

Harold's Suggested Listening Levels
Harold[67] conducted a most comprehensive investigation into the best listening levels for children with hearing defects up to 90 dB. He showed quite conclusively that the practice of adding a fixed increment, such as 30 or 35 dB, to a threshold of detectability, or to an average pure tone hearing loss was a most unsound means of obtaining a best listening level. After constructing articulation curves for 182 children, an attempt was made to devise a method by which suitable volume settings could be predicted from audiograms. Consideration was given to three intensity levels in the proximity of the best one and the following levels were found to represent the point of maximum score or within 90 per cent of maximum score, for 80 per cent of the cases:

Table 7:1
B.B HAROLD'S SUGGESTED LISTENING LEVELS

Hearing Loss	Optimum Listening Level
Between 30-50	80 dB above the normal threshold of detectability
Between 50-75	90 dB above the normal threshold of detectability
Between 75-90	100 dB above the normal threshold of detectability
Greater than 90	The loudest level that could be comfortably tolerated

Harold was careful to point out that a formula that was accurate only four times out of five could not be recommended for general application. He suggested, however, that it might prove useful in situations where it was not possible to apply other methods to ascertain optimum listening levels and it certainly has. Because his sample contained few children whose hearing losses exceeded 90 dB, Harold was unable to make any firm statement about best levels for this group. He did say, however, that "It would seem that for the most part, these cases responded best to speech at the loudest level they could comfortably tolerate. Another important factor that Harold's investigation emphasised was that the intensity range over which sensorineurally deafened children heard best was in most cases a very limited one. Of the 155 children in the group whose losses were sensorineural in origin: 43 per cent obtained their maximum score at one level only; 25 per cent obtained their best score or within 10 percent of maximum at two levels 10 dB apart; and the remaining 32 per cent attained maximum score or within 10 percent of maximum at three levels, i.e., over a range of 20 dB (percentages quoted are approximate).

Silverman reported that thresholds of discomfort, tickle and pain rose systematically and significantly with successive test sessions. Huizing also suggested that tolerance levels could be raised by approximately 10 dB over a period of weeks. Harold drew attention to the difficulty of obtaining an "unvarying criterion for discomfort, particularly with naïve listeners". He considered that many of the low discomfort levels recorded in his research may have been a reflection of the psychological approach to the stimulus rather than the result of "pathological disturbances". Evidence to support this contention is easy to obtain, particularly with the profoundly and sub-totally deaf children. When setting the listening level for these children using a speech training aid, the intensity is often carefully increased, in 5 dB steps. Very frequently the children will grimace or say "too loud" within 5 dB of their threshold of detectability, but if, after a few minutes of talking to the child at this level, the output is unobtrusively increased, they frequently accept the higher level without complaint. When, for example, this technique was used in a study of twenty children with impairments in excess of 100 dB,[26] all but four were tested at a level of 135 dB above 20 μPa and of these four, two preferred 130 dB and two, 125.

Whilst agreeing with the statements by Silverman and Huizing that the initial level of discomfort is lower than that achieved later, it has been my experience with very deaf children that levels of amplification can often be raised in a matter of minutes rather than weeks. Many such children are naïve to sound - in not a few cases they are found not wearing aids "because they are too deaf", or the aids with which they have been issued are not sufficiently powerful to reach them, or have an unsatisfactory frequency response. For the children whose losses were less severe, Lidén, Bangs and Pickles suggested an increase above their thresholds of detectability of a set amount - the former 35 dB (except for recruiting cases), and the two last named, 30 dB. Harold, however, found that there were wide individual differences in the amount of amplification above detectability required. For example, a child whose hearing impairment was 35 dB might require 45 dB of amplification, while one whose loss was 90 dB might require only 10 dB above his threshold of detectability to obtain maximum intelligibility.

Harolds' work suggests that the only reliable method to obtain the optimum level of amplification is to test each child individually. In those cases where speech tests prove impracticable, e.g., due to immaturity of the subject and/or an extremely limited vocabulary, the scale suggested by him, provided its limitations are recognised, seems most likely to obtain the best volume setting.

Just how accurately do deaf children set the volume controls of their hearing aids when they are asked to switch them on? An experiment was conducted with thirty-one partially and severely deaf children to help ascertain this. The age range of the group was between ten and fifteen years and then mean hearing loss 66.11 dB, S.D. 13.5 dB. An articulation curve was made for each child to find his best listening level. He was then asked to tell the investigator (who used a bracketing technique) when the hearing aid was set at the best listening level. (The speech circuit of an audiometer was used for both the articulation curves and the subjective adjustments of the volume control*.)

It was found that the majority of these children set the volume control very near to their best listening level (Fig. 7:2). This agrees with Carhart's finding with 413 adults mentioned earlier. In ten cases, the level was chosen which coincided exactly with the optimum listening level as determined by the articulation tests. A further twelve choices were within 5 dB of the optimum and six were within 10 dB. The difference between these two sets of levels was not statistically significant (t = .38).

Two of the three remaining children chose 15 dB below their best level, and one preferred a level 20 dB above that at which he had obtained maximum articulation score.

Fig. 7:2

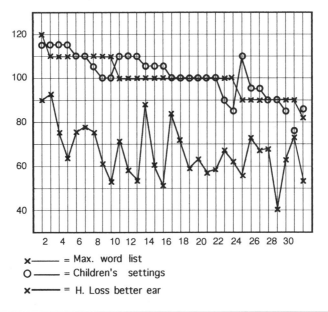

* Speech circuits of audiometers have been adjusted to conform with audiometric zero (i.e., normal threshold of detectability).

Fig 7:3

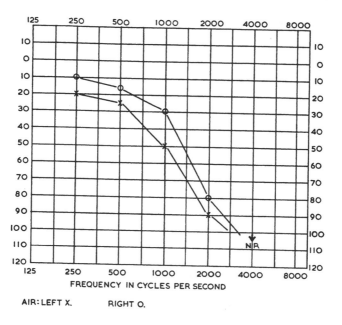

AIR: LEFT X.   RIGHT O.

The audiograms of the three children who set the amplification most inaccurately were consulted. The two children who chose the level 15 dB below the best listening level (Nos. 23 and 30) had slight impairments at 250 Hz which deteriorated rapidly in the higher frequencies (Figs. 7:3 and 7:4).

Fig. 7:4

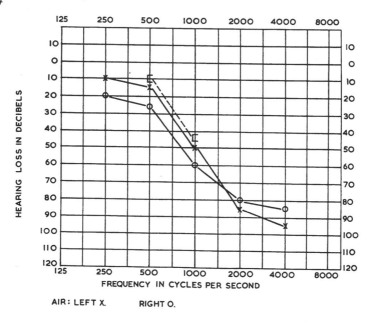

AIR: LEFT X.   RIGHT O.

Child No.25, on the other hand, who set the control 20 dB above the lowest level at which he obtained maximum score, was seen to have the relatively rare shape of audiogram, with a fairly severe impairment over the lower frequency range and a rise (of 20 dB in one octave for sounds between 1,000 and 2,000 Hz).

Fig. 7:5

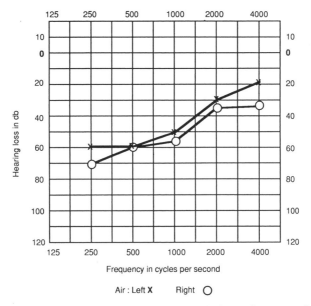

Air : Left **X**   Right O

All three children were rated by their teachers as being of average intelligence. Further investigation of children who possess audiograms that slope steeply from the low to the higher frequencies, tend to confirm the findings of the first two cases cited above. A probable explanation is that the near normal hearing for low sounds makes them unpleasantly loud when amplified, and as a consequence such children quite understandably sacrifice a little intelligibility for a little comfort.

It seems possible that children with hearing losses that are less severe for the higher frequencies (like that shown in the right ear of Child No.24) should not be troubled by increased amplification since sounds above 2,000 Hz are not the strongest in speech and in consequence their amplification should not cause discomfort.

N.B. With preschool children who have had little experience with hearing aids, parents and teachers must give very careful attention to hearing aid output settings since these young children have been found happily to accept levels that are widely at variance with the optimum.

In the senior class of a nursery school for the deaf in London, however, where the children were seven years of age with hearing losses between 60 and 90 dB and had had several years experience of hearing aids, the majority appeared to have developed a considerable degree of skill in setting amplification levels. They would babble into the microphone of the group hearing aid or their individual aid and at the same time adjust the volume control. They would also report faults in their hearing aids very promptly.

SETTING LISTENING LEVELS

Using a speech training hearing aid or the speech circuit of an audiometer (See Figs 1:16 and 17 and 2:1A and B), first manipulate the controls whilst one listens to the output to ensure that the instrument is performing satisfactorily (e.g., 115 dB on a speech training hearing aid, is the level of a fairly loud shout. In audiometers whose speech circuits are begun at the normal threshold of detectability, rather than 20 μPa, the same level of loudness will be reached at 100 dB.

1. Calculate the average hearing loss of the ear to be tested (Average of 500, 1,000 and 2,000 Hz).

2. Using Dr. Harold's table, calculate what the child's best listening level is likely to be:

   e.g., 65, 80, 90 dB = $\frac{235}{3}$ = 78 dB average of 80 dB (to the nearest 5 dB)

   and the optimum listening levels one would expect to be the most satisfactory for this ear, would be 115 dB on a speech training hearing aid and 100 dB on an audiometer.

3. Ask the child to set the output of the hearing aid for the better ear and compare this setting with ones calculated level.

4. If almost identical, accept the child's level and begin a speech test. If widely different, persuade the child to accept a point nearer to Harold's suggested threshold.

5. When children are able to set their listening levels for both ears accurately on a speech training hearing aid, they can usually do so with their individual aids also.

6. Finally encourage children to inform teachers and parents when aids seem not to be performing adequately.

YOUNG DEAF CHILDREN

When one comes to apply this useful information to the wearer of an individual hearing aid, however, one is often immediately in difficulties. The volume controls of wearable hearing aids are seldom marked in decibels and it is often not easy for teachers to ascertain what the output of the aid is at each setting.

Fig. 7:6

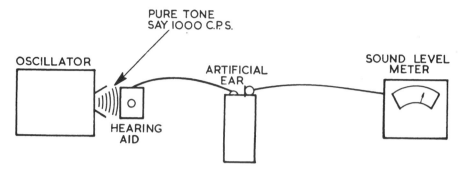

One solution is to have every hearing aid placed on an artificial ear (Figs. 7:6 and 7:7), but at present teachers outside North America frequently do not have ready access to these data. It is recommended *"Wherever possible every hearing aid issued to a child should have with it technical data about the response curve of the instrument and the output that it provides at each position on the volume control when fitted with a new battery."*

The artificial ear (more recently described as the *hearing aid analyser*), as shown in Fig. 7:7, also contains an audiometer. This is able to perform standard audiometric tests such as air and bone conduction measurements and speech audiometry. All the above results can be printed out on an integral printer.

Fig. 7:7. The Hearing Aid Analyser (previously called an artificial ear)

Where such information is not available, however, teachers and clinical workers must fall back on cruder but nevertheless useful subjective tests.

A teacher can, for example, ask an intelligent older child with an identical audiogram, to set the output of the preschool child's aid. When no audiogram is available for the preschooler, it is possible:

1. To use a speech training aid or an audiometer as a monitoring device, to give oneself an idea of a certain level, e.g., 100 dB above 20 μpa.

2. Without looking at the volume control, switch the hearing aid to what seems to be the same level on it.

3. To note the point and repeat steps 1 and 2 several times.

4. To find other levels on the hearing aid control switch in the same manner.

One soon learns that although a hearing aid volume control may be marked from, say, 1 to 5, the output does not always increase in graded steps throughout this range. Sometimes, for example, an aid gives no amplification at all at positions 1 and 2, then a sudden increase to position 3 which is maintained at this level through setting 4 and perhaps has a further increase in output at position 5. Teachers and parents should be aware of any peculiarities that exist in the children's hearing aid outputs. As suggested earlier they should never be afraid to "have a listen" to any child's hearing aid or piece of amplifying apparatus.

Some teachers have an ear piece made for themselves so that they are able to monitor each child's hearing aid performance more accurately (and hygienically!) than when simply holding the receiver or the receiver and ear piece to ones ear.

One further significant fact for teachers and audiologists dealing with young children to note, is that hearing aid performance is normally obtained by using a 2.0 c.c coupler as this is considered to be near the dimension of the average adult external auditory meatus. In children, however, the smaller the size of the ear canal, the greater the increase in sound energy (See Fig. 7:8). For example, 6 dB should be added to the artificial ear output readings when the volume between the earmould tip and the ear drum is 1.00 c.c. and a further 6 dB should be added when this volume is reduced to 0.5 c.c.

Such over amplification may well cause these young children significant discomfort and represents a further reason for some children's rejection of their aids. Suggestions are made in Chapter 10 for supervising and maintaining hearing aids.

Fig. 7:8

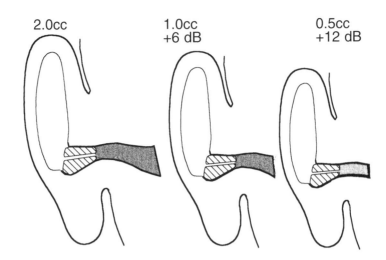

In summary, there are five points that should be borne in mind with regards listening levels if the most intelligent use is to be made of hearing aids:

1. *The listening level should be set as accurately as possible.* It will be remembered that nearly half of the cases studied by Harold heard best at one point only - 10 dB above or below this level caused a significant dropping off in the scores obtained.

2. *Older partially and severely deaf children seem in most cases to set the volume of their hearing aids with extreme accuracy.* The implication of this is not that checking listening levels with older children is unnecessary, but that such a check need not be made daily or even weekly after the initial best level has been determined.

3. *It is possible to increase levels of comfort with profoundly and sub-totally deaf subjects - particularly if they are naïve listeners.* It is suggested here, that one should not accept the first level indicated by these very deaf children, but should experiment after a few minutes with levels 5 or even 10 dB above the first level. This ensures that such subjects are then listening at "the loudest level they can comfortably tolerate".

4. *Younger deaf children frequently have very little idea of best listening levels.* The setting of volume controls is in consequence a very important part of the work of teachers, parents and others who deal with young deaf children.

5. *Input increases as volume of canal decreases* (See Fig. 7:5 above). Thus an aid which is delivering 100 dB to an adolescent child, might deliver 106 dB to a 6 year old child and 112 dB to an infant who wears the same instrument on the same setting. (Now please re-read all of Point 1 again.)

Chapter 8

LOUDNESS RECRUITMENT AND
AUDITORY TEMPORAL ACUITY

Loudness Recruitment

In 1924, Pohlman and Krantz reported than some hearing impaired patients experienced "a near normal sensation of loudness" when a tone was raised above their auditory threshold levels. This phenomenon has become known as *loudness recruitment.*

One of the best definitions of loudness recruitment is that of Hirsh, Palva and Goodman[73] who describe it as "a more than normal increase in subjective loudness for a given increase in physical intensity". To put it another way, a patient with recruitment, in spite of an impairment at threshold, hears loud sounds with a sensation of loudness equal or nearly equal to the loudness with which a normal ear would perceive them. There have been a large number of theories of what causes recruitment, but none seems yet to have been generally accepted. The hearing theory of Lorente de No (quoted by Nilsson) is often used to give a theoretical explanation of recruitment occurring in all forms of nerve

Fig. 8:1

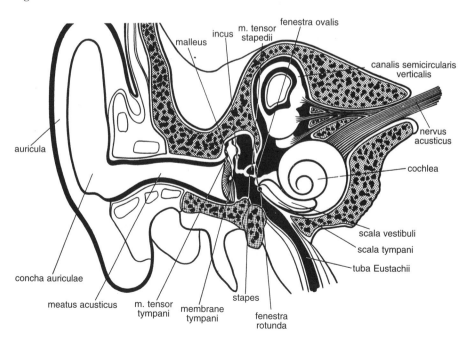

deafness. The theory is applied in this way. Where there has been damage to some of the neurones, there is a loss of sensitivity to sounds of low intensity, but where the intensity of the sound is high, other neurones will come into play to fill the demand, and the cortex will receive a sound equal in loudness to that of a normal ear. Since a slightly different pathway is used, the sound received may be qualitatively different from the original signal. Some recruiting patients, for example, report a change in the pitch of the sound, etc.

Numerous workers gave favourable consideration to hair cell theories but felt that the absence of recruitment in cases of deafness caused by eighth nerve tumours precluded the acceptance of these.

Fig. 8:2

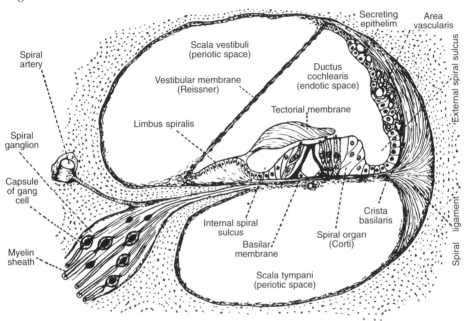

Harold,[67] too, produced evidence to suggest that recruitment was a result of malfunction of some part of the end organ or hearing, and could not find its presence in cases of eighth nerve disorders or cortical lesions.

Loudness recruitment is an interesting phenomenon, which can be of considerable significance to audiologists and otologists for diagnostic purposes. For teachers of the deaf and speech therapists, however, recruitment is of very little importance, and if they are conversant with the following three facts about it, it is really all that is necessary to know. (a) Full or partial recruitment seems to be present in about two-thirds of the children in schools and classes for the deaf and partially hearing, (b) if anything, children with recruitment tend to hear "better" than those without it, and (c) thresholds of discomfort are not lowered due to the presence of recruitment. It is commonly believed that children who do not seem able to tolerate loud sounds are suffering from recruitment, but in Dr Harold's study, this proved not to be so.

The information contained in this section has been obtained very largely from the unpublished work of Dr. B.B. Harold, [67] with his kind permission.

E.P. Fowler,[59] as early as 1928, also drew attention to the recruitment phenomenon. He observed that some patients with normal hearing in one ear and a considerable loss in the other sometimes heard a loud sound equally well in either ear. He devised a means of measuring this effect by allowing the patient to listen alternately with either ear while he increased the intensity. At a certain level, the sounds were heard equally loudly in both ears if recruitment was present (See Fig. 8:3). His technique is known as the alternate binaural loudness balance test, and several loudness balance tests have been developed from it. S.N. Reger, for example, showed that recruitment could be demonstrated using one ear only as long as at least two frequencies had a large difference in threshold values.

Fig. 8:3

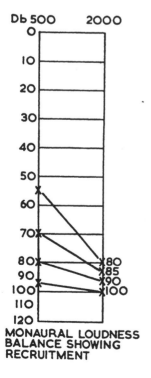

MONAURAL LOUDNESS
BALANCE SHOWING
RECRUITMENT

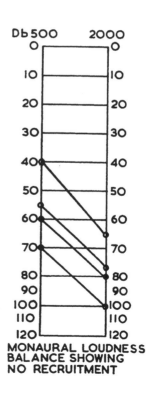

MONAURAL LOUDNESS
BALANCE SHOWING
NO RECRUITMENT

DeBruine Altes after a careful study suggested that although it was not easy for an untrained ear to judge whether the loudness of two tones of different frequency were equal, was of the opinion that the nearer in frequency the tones being compared, the more accurate the test result was likely to be.

The method of recording the loudness balance test results as adopted by Fowler helps to make clear the effect of the recruitment phenomenon. (Moore et al, in 1984, used 2 diagrams illustrating the fact that as the intensity of the stimulus sound increased, the sensation of loudness increased more rapidly for subjects with hearing losses). Fowler showed that by the time the sound was of approximately 80 dB or 10 100 dB , both recruiting and normally hearing subjects were experiencing virtually equal sensations of loudness. Two vertical lines were printed on the record sheet, each scaled in 10 dB steps from zero to 120. On the second line the values of the reference tones used in the test and on the first are recorded the intensities of the test tones for which judgements of equal loudness had been made. Lines then joined each equal loudness judgement with its appropriate reference tone.

Fig. 8:4

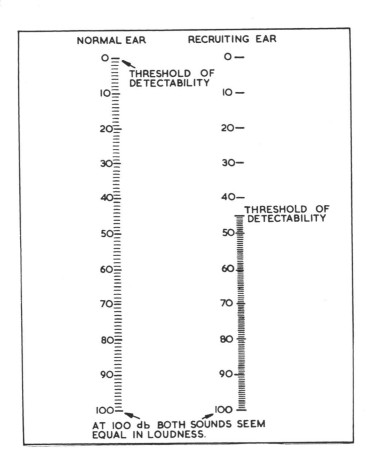

Numerous tests for recruitment have been devised in addition to those involving loudness balance techniques. A type that has been given favourable consideration by a large number of workers, however, is that which involves the difference limen for intensity. *The difference limen is the minimum increment in stimulus needed to produce a noticeable difference in sensation.*

According to Bangs and Mullins, the rationale behind all types of tests using the limen as a method of measuring loudness recruitment, is that the number of loudness units (difference limena) from the detectability of a sound to a sensation of equal loudness is approximately the same for both a normal and a recruiting ear, and since the threshold of the recruiting ear is elevated, the size of the difference limen must be smaller (See Fig. 8:4). The argument is supported by experimental evidence, as for example in the work of von Békèsy[9] (*See Endnotes p124). It has been found that recruiting patients *are* more sensitive to slight changes in sound intensity. Where normal and non-recruiting ears are only able to detect changes of about 1 dB or more, a person with recruitment can detect changes of as little as .3 dB, and occasionally even less than this.

Von Békèsy designed a special audiometer for his test. With it the subject records his/her own audiogram by noting the point at which a tone becomes audible and the point where it becomes just inaudible. The tone presented constantly changes in frequency. The recorded graph (See Figs. 8:5A and 8:5B) of the subject's responses show the relative size of the difference limen at threshold.

In this test, a pure tone that varies in intensity is presented to the subject. If this variation is great - say 3dB - we all hear it as a beating tone. As the amount of intensity change is reduced, the sound to normal ears gradually loses its sensation of *beat* and is heard as a tone of constant intensity. As has been stated, however, recruiting subjects with their small difference limena, can detect much smaller variations in intensity than can those without recruitment.
Denes and Naunton[43] devised a somewhat similar test, and Jerger[85] combined some of the features of both tests to evolve a new technique using an ascending method of presentation, i.e., the subject listened first to a constant tone and the amplitude modulation was increased until it was observed as a beat.
In Békèsy audiometry, the test tone begins at 100 Hz and moves across the whole range of frequencies to 8,000 Hz. The level of loudness of the test tone is controlled by the patient. He/she is asked to press the signal switch whenever a sound is heard, and to release the switch as soon as it becomes inaudible.

Békèsy audiometers reduce the level of the signal as soon as the patient presses the switch and gradually increase the level as soon as the switch is released. The resultant audiograms indicate the presence or absence of recruitment and non-organic hearing loss etc. (See Figs. 8:5A and 8:5B)

Fig. 8:5

A

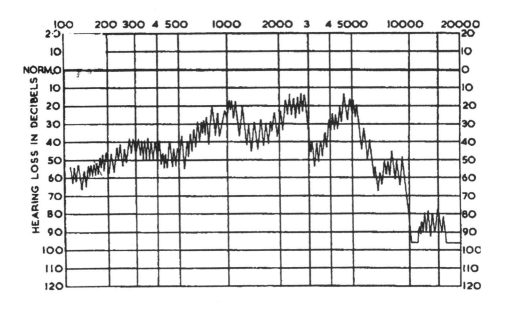

B

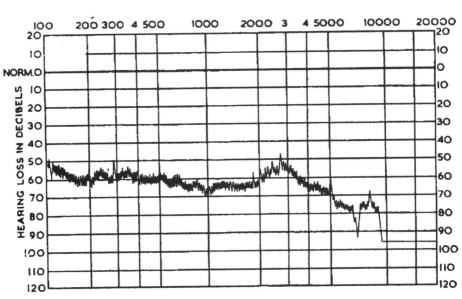

Although a wide variety of tests is available, the detection of recruitment is often difficult and uncertain. In consequence, many workers have listed symptoms of the phenomenon that can be used in the clinical situation as a supplement the more formal tests. Unfortunately, there is not always agreement of such symptoms being a true indication of the presence or absence of recruitment.

The following symptoms have been suggested:

1. *High Threshold Discrimination for Pure Tone Audiometry.*
   Since the recruiting subject has a smaller difference limen than one with a non-recruiting ear, the margin between hearing and not hearing will be narrow and he thus often responds to threshold tests quickly and with confidence.

2. *Sudden Decrease in Speech Reception Capacity.*
   A slight increase in threshold loss will bring about a loss in capacity to hear speech out of all proportion to the increase in deafness.

3. *Lack of Voice Control when Trying on a Hearing Aid for the First Time.*
   The explanation of this occurrence as a symptom of recruitment is as follows: The patient's voice, being near the microphone, is of higher intensity than that of the speaker some feet away, and this being so, recruitment may occur for the higher intensity but not for the lower, thus causing an "abnormally large" discrepancy between the loudness of the two voices. The sudden, unexpected loudness of the patient's own voice causes him to lose the normal control he has over his own voice and sometimes may cause confusion which prevents him from speaking at all.

4. A close correspondence between the frequency of spontaneous otoacoustic emissions (SOAE's) and the frequency of the predominant matching tone of *tinnitus* (see below), has been the most commonly used criterion for establishing the presence of tinnitus in patients (Hazell[69,70] Rebillard et al.[122], Zwicker[157] and Zwicker and Schloth[158]).

   The presence of *tinnitus* (ringing in the ears), diplacusis (hearing a sound of higher pitch in the recruiting ear than in the non-recruiting ear), *low tolerance for loud sounds,* and *vertigo* (dizziness) have all been *attributed* to loudness recruitment - frequently, it must be said, without a great deal of scientific evidence). Others have noted that people with recruitment frequently complain that "voices sound 'tinny', 'fuzzy' or 'hollow' or in other ways distorted". A commonly held misconception is that "all subjects who have a low tolerance for loud sound are suffering from recruitment".

Although *some* subjects with recruitment *do* have lower tolerance than normal, this is certainly not true in every case and many of those most experienced in studying this phenomenon believe that there is very little difference in levels of tolerance between recruiting and non-recruiting subjects.

Aetiology and Recruitment

The earlier workers in the field were interested in the loudness balance test as a means of distinguishing between sensorineural and conductive deafnesses - the presence of recruitment indicating a sensorineural deafness and its absence, deafness due to a problem in the conductive mechanism, i.e. a conductive hearing loss. They believed that the results of tuning fork tests and bone conduction audiometry were often misleading, particularly in cases of unilateral deafness (or whenever there was considerable difference in acuity between the two ears), because of cross conduction.

Dix, Hallpike and Hood,[45] who in 1948 reported on the results of loudness balance tests given to thirty patients with Ménière's disease and twenty patients with deafness caused by degeneration of the eighth nerve owing to pressure of infiltration by tumours. At that time it was generally believed that recruitment was present in all cases of nerve deafness. These writers found recruitment present and complete in all cases of Ménière's disease and completely absent in fourteen of the eighth nerve deafness cases with slight recruitment in the remaining six cases. They believed that recruitment was due to degeneration of the hair cells in the organ of Corti and that the loudness balance test could be used as a technique for distinguishing between deafness involving the cochlear, which would show recruitment and deafness caused by nerve involvement beyond the cochlear for which there would be no recruitment. The slight recruitment displayed by some cases with deafness caused by disorders of the eighth nerve was explained in terms of secondary cochlear involvement caused by interference with cochlea blood supply.

Fowler[53] and Huizing disagreed with the finding of Dix, Hallpike and Hood, that recruitment was characteristically absent in cases of deafness caused by retrocochlear lesions. The finding however, has since been confirmed by a large number of workers.

If, as seems likely, recruitment does occur only in the cochlear, the determination of its presence can be seen to represent a very useful aid to the diagnosis of various deafnesses.

RECRUITMENT AND HEARING FOR SPEECH

Finally, what effect does loudness recruitment have on a patient's hearing for speech? Until the 1960's it was generally thought that is was detrimental. Harold found on examining the aetiologies of the cases used by previous workers, however, that a very large proportion were deaf as a result of Ménière's disease. This is a perceptive condition of adulthood and it has been well established that all such cases recruit and all hear speech badly. Harold contended, therefore, that this preponderance of Ménière's disease cases in each research group gave the impression that all *recruiting* cases heard speech poorly. He found no significant difference between the hearing for speech of recruiting non-recruiting cases in the adult group, and in the children's group, those with recruitment heard speech significantly better than did those who were non-recruiting.*

TINNITUS

Tinnitus may be described as "The Perception of sound originating within the head in the absence of any auditory stimulation".

Causes of Tinnitus

Two types of tinnitus have been identified - that which lasts a short time and persistent tinnitus which caused sufferers considerable distress. The latter was often triggered (or made worse), by emotional events such as bereavements, work or family stresses, etc. Persistence of tinnitus was frequently accompanied by feelings of hopelessness and/or despair because it seemed that nothing could be done about the condition. This ignored the fact, however, that the majority of people with hearing losses did suffer from tinnitus. Although tinnitus is twice as common among hearing impaired people than in the normally hearing population, this is not because the inner ear is damaged. The perception and loudness of tinnitus depends on whether the brain is able to suppress these sounds or whether it amplifies them because of their importance as a real or potential threat.

It is of interest that when deaf children are questioned about tinnitus, they will frequently indicate in a somewhat bored manner, "Oh yes, it is there often" or "Many times". Presumably its presence has become so familiar that it is not felt to be worthy of mention. Adventitiously deafened adults, however, discuss this condition quite frequently and report that it is more pronounced when they become tired, and that a cup of tea sometimes seems to reduce it. Goodey (1982) made the observation that "many drugs and some foods can cause or aggravate tinnitus in some patients". He recommended that such substances should be identified and withdrawn. Goodey had also found that hypotensives, antibiotics, flouride or thyroxine drugs could temporarily reduce tinnitus. *Intravenous lignocaine* could reduce and even eliminate it in some subjects, but could also aggravate it in others and have no effect at all in a third group. The most successful cases treated with lignocaine appeared to be those whose deafness originated in the cochlear.

Two centres, one in New York and one in London, have recently had very

---

* Discussion with Dr Harold - 28.8.90

considerable success in assisting tinnitus patients. These were in the Yale University Medical Centre under Professor P.J. Jastreboff and colleagues and in University College, London, where Mr. Jonathan Hazell, FRCS and a multidisciplinary team of scientists have been able to minimise the effect of tinnitus in many patients and completely eradicate it in others.[70,71]

Patients had come to these centres complaining of sounds that were heard "in the ears" or "in the head" - buzzing, ringing, whistling, hissing, pulsing and other sounds that *did not come from an external source*. Tinnitus emerged for relatively short periods in young people after attending discos where sound levels were usually excessively loud, but also after a period of listening in a quiet room. The specialists considered tinnitus a natural phenomenon experienced by 90% or more of the population and that it normally went away after a short time. (It was, however, emphasised to the patients that loud continuous sound, could, of course, damage the listener's hearing).

Jastreboff and Hazell have been responsible for retraining programmes for tinnitus sufferers being set up around the world.

Hazell and his associates have developed a protocol for the clinical treatment of tinnitus after careful assessment. A strategy of investigation and reassurance operates which is based on the patient's understanding of the underlying mechanisms involved in tinnitus generation. Other courses have been established for one day a week treatment in various parts of the British Isles.

Most of the treatment is aimed at bringing about a process of *habituation* (which occurs naturally in the majority of people experiencing tinnitus over a long period of time).

Retraining therapy:
The treatment was based on the new understandings of tinnitus mechanisms found by Professor Jastreboff. It was necessary to retrain the subconscious "filters" which had become "trained" to focus on the weak signals coming from the inner ear.

First, careful use of hearing aids had to be applied to each ear to minimise any listening strain.

Next, low level white noise (not masking) was used to increase the activity of the auditory filters. Hazell stressed that it was vital to change ideas based on the concept that tinnitus was due to ear damage, to dead hair cells or the like and to learn that tinnitus was due to altered filtering of signals from the ear by the brain and that these filters can be reset so that they transmit messages to the hearing cortex (the conscious part) and this results in tinnitus no longer being heard.

Symptom control is required in almost half of the patients seen at the University College clinic and various techniques are discussed including prosthetic masking devices, psychological approaches, drug therapy and electrical tinnitus suppression. (Children can often be trained in one session[†]).

"The earlier one can obtain reassurance about tinnitus the sooner it will cease to be a problem".

A number of hospital ENT departments in Britain now have a special interest in tinnitus and run a tinnitus clinic on one day each week. (Information about these may be obtained on the RNID Tinnitus Helpline).

AUDITORY TEMPORAL ACUITY
In addition to studies of a listener's ability to detect smaller and smaller differences in intensity and frequency of sounds, interesting work has been done in the *temporal* field. If 2 sounds are presented to a person with a 1/2 second interval between them, they can clearly be perceived as 2 sounds. When these same sounds are produced closer and closer together, there comes a point where they appear to "run together" and are perceived by the listener as just one sound. The point at which this "running together" or *fusion* occurs, differs in different listeners. A second and some suggest, better, technique for studying this phenomenon, is to begin with 2 sounds being produced very close together, and gradually to increase the interval between them until they are perceived as 2 sounds. The point at which this occurs is known as auditory temporal *fission*.

Boothroyd compared the auditory and tactile temporal acuity of 3 groups of subjects. The first were 5 normally hearing students, the second group were 5 severely deaf subjects with high frequency hearing losses (ISO thresholds at 2,000 and 4,000 Hz of less than 100 dB) and 5 profoundly deaf subjects without high frequency hearing. Subjects were tested by hand, using a bone conduction vibrator, and by ear (monoaurally) using a TDH49 earphone.

This showed that all 3 groups had very similar thresholds when tested in the hand. The profoundly deaf group, however, performed much less well at the ear than in the hand.

The use of hearing aids by such profoundly deaf subjects is often justified because of the reception of limited cues, such as voicing, which might provide a supplement to lipreading. Since many voiced/voiceless consonant discriminations require a temporal resolution in the order of approximately 20 m.sec., it seemed to other writers that the temporal acuity of the pathological ear might impose a limit on the potential value of residual hearing. This conclusion might be somewhat speculative in view of the small samples and the differences of only 5 m.sec. involved between successful and unsuccessful temporal resolution. Research in the 1970's, however, indicated that the perception of fine auditory-temporal events might well represent a crucial skill in both the reception and production of intelligible spoken language.

A useful research was undertaken by Dr. Richard Stoker, (himself profoundly deaf from birth) while studying at Salford University in Manchester and is quoted at considerable length below. Forty two pupils at two schools for deaf children were used to test the hypothesis of the three studies mentioned above, that severely hearing impaired individuals who could demonstrate accurate auditory temporal acuity, would also demonstrate better speech production abilities. The subjects were asked to report the number of discrete sounds (tones heard in a pair of stimuli separated by a randomly varied time interval. By comparing the subjects' responses over a number of trials, it was possible to determine the point at which auditory temporary "*fission*" occurred (i.e. that point or length of gap between the 2 sound stimuli, here the subject distinctly heard 2 sounds).

The children for the tests were selected on the basis that they had a mean hearing loss over the 3 speech frequencies (500, 1,000 and 2,000 Hz) of 70 dB or greater. The mean was 90.3 dB. Other constraints were that the children were prelingually deaf and none had concomitant intellectual or emotional problems.

Test stimuli were pre-recorded on a Ferrograph Type Y722 magnetic tape recorder. They were produced from 2 data pulse type 401 function generators whose outputs fed into electronic switches controlled by modular logic and Grason Stadler 1200 series timers. The frequency, intensity and duration of the test stimuli were monitored during preparation of the tape by a headphone articulated with a B and K type 4152 artificial ear.

Stimuli pairs were recorded at equal intensity and the same frequency (500 Hz). They were 250 m.sec. in length and no rise or delay period was provided so that the sounds were rather like "clicks" or a single "plop" - depending upon the interval between the stimuli. One hundred and sixty stimulus pairs were recorded with intervals that varied randomly among the following values: 1, 2, 3, 5, 7, 10, 30, 50, 70 and 100 m.sec.

Speech
Tape recordings of each child's vocalisations in responses to visual stimuli were taken. The stimuli were cards containing common objects in colour. The subject was asked to name the object and describe the colour, e.g. "The cake is white and brown".

The words and colours were chosen so that virtually all English phonemes would be included in initial, medial and final positions. Ratings of the subjects' speech were made by a panel of 4 listeners who were required to mark on a form whether they were able to understand the key words (object and colour). From these data it was possible to compute a percentage intelligibility score. Earlier studies had shown that ratings obtained under circumstances similar to those described above correlated highly with ratings obtained using much more elaborate testing procedures. (These studies of Asp and Subtelny were responsible for the writer developing his Articulation and Rate of Utterance tests of speech intelligibility (Appendix 2:5).

Results
Results were plotted for each subject and have been shown in Figs. 8:6 and 8:7. The time (in milliseconds) at which the children were able to detect 2 tones rather than 1, have been plotted by the writer, firstly for one subject and in Fig 8:7, for all of Stoker's subjects.

Fig. 8:6

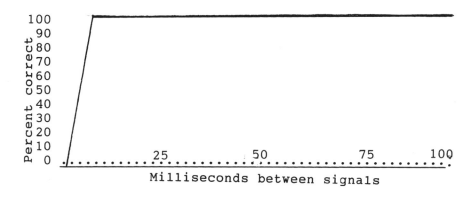

It is interesting that Stoker found 2 definite groups where this discrimination (or "*fission*") occurred. This *bimodal* distribution is shown in Fig. 8:7 (writer's adaptation). Nineteen subjects obtained 100% discrimination within the range of 1 to 5 milliseconds, but 23 were well beyond that time distance. These 23 children required gaps between tones of between 20 and 30 milliseconds before they could indicate that 2 tones had definitely occurred.

Fig. 8:7

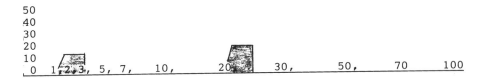

```
50
40
30
20
10
 0    1, 2, 3,  5, 7,  10,      20    30,    50,    70     100
```

It is of even more interest, that Stoker was able to show that the 19 subjects in Group I who could detect very brief gaps between 2 tones were also able *to speak more intelligibly* - 72.7% rather than 52.6% for Group II of 23 children with less precise auditory temporal acuity (t = 3.085, p. 0.005).

Stoker's conclusion was that hearing impaired children who were adept at auditory temporal acuity tasks also demonstrated better speech production ability. He felt that the implications of his research when viewed with other data suggested that auditory perception in time was more important in reference to speech production than were frequency or intensity discrimination.

The above research in auditory temporal acuity has been quoted at some length as it has been little researched in the United Kingdom and if Stoker's suggestion that it is of such significance in the speech production of deaf children is valid then it should be researched further by psychologists, audiologists and speech therapists. The effect of training might well be studied. It certainly adds to knowledge in the speech production and reception of hearing impaired subjects and helps account for some of the "unusual" results achieved by individual children in these areas, e.g. two children with identical audiograms for pure tones, hearing similar amounts of speech and one speaking less intelligibly than another after similar speech training.[33]

John and Howarth[88] emphasised the importance of time in both the production and perception of intelligible speech by deaf children. This is clearly one of the reasons for the success of the Ewings' Listening Reading Speaking (LRS) method (See Chapter 10 below). This has been found an excellent technique for presenting both language and speech to deaf children. It also assists their reading, of course, since all lessons begin with a passage (or phrase) of written language. This is a tremendous help to those children who do not speech-read well.

It has been found that from the age of six years, children are able to make accurate decisions regarding temporal acuity with both high and low frequency tones, as accurately as adult listeners.

There is a possibility that the poorer results achieved by some children on auditory temporal acuity tasks, may be due to some central (cortical) involvement.

Endnotes

* Dr. Békèsy was later awarded a Nobel Prize for his exceptional work in the audiological and otological fields.

† Discussion with Mr. Jonathan Hazell, F.R.C.S., London, 13th February 1997

Chapter 9

EARMOULDS

"Hearing aids are only as useful as the earmoulds allow them to be."

No matter how sophisticated an individual hearing aid happens to be, if it is attached to or placed within an unsatisfactory earmould, much of the aid's performance may be dissipated or distorted before the signal reaches the wearer's eardrum.

Northern and Downs[110] described earmoulds as "an essential feature of the hearing aid system".

Perhaps the commonest cause of concern with earmoulds has been their enabling sound to leak around the edges of the mould and be re-amplified again and again by the microphone (Nolan - 1982 Northern and Downs - 1984)[110]. Almost immediately, this amplified leakage of energy is heard as a whistling sound - *acoustic feedback*. In the past, the production of unsatisfactory earmoulds has placed whole hearing aid programmes in jeopardy. When an aid feeds back, the speech signal is usually so distorted that a child should be asked to switch the aid off until an efficient mould can be fitted.

Making Ear Moulds
Since individual hearing aids have been produced which require earpieces to be inserted in the ear, the making of accurate earmoulds has frequently caused real concern to parents, teachers, audiologists and of course, to the deaf children themselves. Mercifully, poorly fitting earmoulds in many areas today, are rare. Even with young children whose external ears are soft, delicate and constantly growing larger, success can be achieved in nearly every case. (It has to be accepted that new ear moulds will be required by these little children 4 or even 5 times each year as a result of the rapid growth of the ears during this time of life.) With careful impressioning techniques and skillful preparation of the mould, however, almost 100 percent success is achieved by many workers.

A measure of the concern shown by audiologists for the effect that non-sealing earmoulds can have, is reflected in the variety of earmoulds currently on offer and the plethora of adaptations available. The National Acoustics Laboratories in Australia, for example, produce 18 different styles of earmoulds using 9 different materials. Twenty types of venting with 7 varieties of tubing are available. With some 150,000 combinations to choose from, the likelihood of achieving a satisfactory fit for each child seem high, if, of course, one has sufficient time and skill in the selection process.

In 1976, the National Acoustics Laboratories and the Department of Prosthetic Dentistry at the University of Sydney, collaborated to produce excellent ear impressions and earmoulds. (Fifield, et al., 1980)[56]. Teachers, parents and trainee audiologists will find the full text of this article in the Volta Review of January, 1980 (pp. 33-38).

One simple method used with preschool children with considerable success in 1984, was as follows:

> With the mother or class teacher present, the child was asked to sit or lie on a bench at the side of the clinic with his/her head on a small pillow. The teacher then smiled at the child and placed one hand gently but firmly on the side of the heard, leaving the ear exposed.

> It was then a relatively simple matter to place soft earmould material into the ear, press in the spring section of the ring and spring clip and then allow the acrylic material to dry. The operation to this stage had taken less than 3 minutes.

> The earmould was then bored and vented as required and the child could wear the hearing aid home (after the parents had been shown how to care for it and the make the best use of it, or course). This certainly appeared to represent "a giant leap for mankind" compared with many earlier techniques. An audiologist reported 20 years ago, finding himself under his office table with a blob of plaster of Paris on one thumb, as he sought an active little toddler who thought it was a game! Urged on by the mother, he said he had to make somewhat desperate drives at the better ear whenever the child "came into range".

> The "gentle but firm pressure" on the wriggling head of the toddler seemed a significant factor in the former method's success.

Venting of Earmoulds

Accurate earmoulds not only lead sound into the ear, but they also prevent it coming out again. Such occlusion of the outer ear, however, can create a feeling of pressure in the ear and unless one was severely deaf, the wearer's own voice could sound unnatural. For the less deaf, also, the internal sounds made by chewing and swallowing are unintentionally amplified.

Vents in the earmould reduce the amplitude of low frequencies and overcome most of the problems mentioned above. Unfortunately the overall intelligibility of the speech received has not been found to increase significantly as a result of venting.

Points made in the excellent article of D.B.Fifield and his associates (National Acoustics Laboratories, Australia), mentioned above, included 3 major steps in producing reliable ear moulds which did not allow acoustic feed-back to occur even when high gain was required, included the following:

Stage 1 - The primary impression

(a)   A cotton block was attached to a strong thread positioned in the centre of the ear canal.

(b)   A 6cm length of silicone rubber tubing with an internal diameter of 2mm was guided on to the thread and pushed down to the cotton and secured to ensure it did not move back.

(c)   A heavy bodied silicone rubber impressioning material was poured into the canal and concha. This gave an impression of the outer ear and the ear canal.

Stage II - *The Canal build-up*

Medium bodied silicone material was used to apply a thick coating to the surface of the primary impression. The impression was then reseated in the ear before the material had begun to set. Gentle pressure was applied to help the silicone material "flow" and give an accurate impression of the canal and was then allowed to dry and set.

The final operation at this stage was to test the seal by connecting the protruding tube from the impression to the air pump of the impedance meter. The pressure was increased slowly to a maximum of 200mm of water and maintained at that level for 5 seconds. If no loss of pressure was indicated on the manometer, the impression could be said to have achieved a satisfactory seal (See Fig. 3:1). If there was a fall in pressure, the procedure for building up the impression was repeated until it became completely effective.

Stage III - Applying a "Wash"

The final stage was designed to record the fine detail of the ear's structure on the impression. It was also possible to extend the canal at this stage if it was thought to be necessary.

Once again, a cotton block was placed in the ear canal attached to a strong piece of cord which was passed through the tube from the canal side outwards. Thin-bodied silicone material (about the consistence of honey), was syringed into the canal and over the surface of the concha. The impression was then pushed down the thread before the silicone material had set. The impression was then gently removed from the ear.

Fifield, et al. recommended that instructions to the ear mould laboratory should state clearly that the impressions must not be built up or modified. (Thick walled tubing, they said, should be requested routinely for moulds to be used with high powered hearing aids.)

These writers concluded by saying that their 3 stage impressioning technique was suitable for manufacturing all types of earmoulds and for use with all types of earmould materials. Detailed step by step instructions for making these impressions may be obtained by Departments of Health or Education writing to the Director, National Acoustics Laboratories, 5 Hickson Road, Sydney, NSW 2000, Australia, and distributing the information to all of their special schools and Parent-Teacher associations who are dealing with hearing impaired children.

Further practical guidance for those responsible for making earmoulds is contained in Paediatric Audiology (Ed.) McCormick,B[98] Chapter 12 by M. Nolan. Both ear impressioning and making different earmoulds are dealt with in considerable detail.

Killion[94] showed that *venting* of earmoulds was effective for increasing sounds below 1,000 Hz; damping was successful for sounds between 1,000 and 3,000 Hz and to increase sounds above 3,000 Hz, a tapered length of plastic tubing leading from the earpiece of the receiver and running to the microphone of the behind-the-ear aid had been very helpful.

Michael Pollack and Ronald Morgan, in their excellent 50 page chapter entitled *"Earmould Technology and Acoustics"*[119], provided a useful diagram of the outer ear showing its 13 different parts (helix, fosa, concha, tragus etc.). They emphasised that accurate earmoulds should replicate 11 of these 13 indentations and ridges very precisely if successful *shell moulds* were to be made for wearers who required high gain hearing aids. Again thick walled tubing was used to avoid feedback.

Skeleton moulds are similar to shell moulds except that a ring of the acrylic material is left around the back wall of the pinna which helps to retain the mould in place. Skeleton moulds are able to be used with short canal and open bore fittings. Pollack and Morgan indicated that skeleton moulds and variations of them were the most popular earmoulds in use in the United States at that time (1980).

These writers were also able to demonstrate just how much (and occasionally, how little) variation in hearing aid performance occurred as a result of using ear moulds that were made with different shapes and from different materials. The length of the plastic tubing, its diameter and resilience all affected the sounds that are conveyed to the hearing aid wearer's eardrum.

Chapter 10

THE PROVISION OF AUDITORY EXPERIENCE

The Full Time Use of Hearing Aids

Individual aids should be worn in much the same way as many people wear spectacles, i.e., they are the first thing they grope for in the morning and the last thing they take off at night. Children wearing aids should learn to put them on as soon as they have had a wash in the morning and should leave them on - as far as possible - until bedtime at night. Obviously, when swimming, bathing or playing boisterous games, aids must be removed, but at nearly all other times, they should be worn. In very noisy conditions, if wearing the aid becomes too unpleasant, they should *switch* them off rather than *take* them off. Adults will sometimes put the aid on to listen to the radio, remove it while they read a book, put it on again because a visitor has called, take it off to have a meal and so on. Children, too, will often remove the aids because it is an arithmetic lesson or a silent reading lesson. Children or adults who are continually putting their hearing aids on and taking them off, however, rarely make satisfactory use of them. They are really just fooling with the aid,. "Put them on and forget them" should be the maxim. If the aids are worn comfortably, as will be emphasised later, it is not uncommon for wearers to comment that throughout the day they only remember that they have the aid on once or twice.

With the longer hair styles now common among children and young people, hearing aids can be concealed very effectively if that is what one wishes. Ear level and in the canal hearing aids, can, of course, be completely concealed beneath the hair.

Early Fitting. The secret of obtaining ready acceptance of hearing aids is to fit the children as early as possible in life. The hearing aid then becomes so much a part of them, that they wear them as readily as they do their shoes and socks. Procedures helpful in securing the regular use of hearing aids include:-

Adult Interest. Undoubtedly, the modern in the ear or in the canal aids are much more easy to persuade children (and adults) to use than the old body worm aids.

Unless at least one adult will take an interest in the hearing aid, however, it will rarely be worn. Parents, teachers, the hearing aid technicians, the family doctor, brothers and sisters, aunts and uncles, and so on, can all help here. The doctors and aunts, etc., need only to say to the child, "How is the hearing aid going?" It is often a good talking point to begin a conversation with a deaf child if one has not seen him before or if one sees him infrequently, and it certainly helps the child to feel that all sorts of people are pleased to see him/her wearing the aid.

In schools and classes for deaf children, it is *essential* that the *senior teachers* and the *class teachers* recognise the value of hearing aids and give active encouragement to the children and do not just pay lipservice to the idea of the full-time use of hearing aids. Getting deaf children to wear hearing aids is rather like a mathematics or a speech scheme in school - if the principal is not prepared to put his or her weight into seeing that the programme is carefully launched and conscientiously carried out, everyone's task is made much more difficult. The first thing a sceptical head teacher or teacher might do is to take some of the simple tests described in this book and experiment carefully with a number of children until he/she convinces himself/herself of the fact that sound can mean something to almost every child - even in a school for profoundly deaf children.

The principal and teachers should aim at enabling the children to make the most intelligent use of hearing aids in conditions which approximate as nearly as possible to the optimum.

Class teachers have a responsibility to check the performance of individual hearing aids. This serves the dual purpose (a) of ensuring that all aids are performing satisfactorily and (b) of showing the children that the teacher is genuinely interested in their aids. With most nursery and infant school children, checking should be done three times each day and with older children, once a day. "Am I to spend half my day fiddling about with hearing aids then?" says the harassed teacher. The answer is "No, the average time for little children is five minutes a day and for the older ones two minutes." It may be added that even this time is not wasted since it presents a good opportunity for pertinent and meaningful language work.

One method of checking hearing aid performance which has proved quite effective is the following:

Ling's Five Sound Hearing Aid Test: Daniel Ling devised a simple little check for parents and teachers to ensure that the children's hearing aids were functioning properly before they left for school or before lessons began each morning and afternoon. The 5 phonemes [a, u, i, ʃ and s] were said in a clear voice when the child was not watching. His/her response was simply to clap his/her hands or tap on a table whenever a sound was heard. These 5 sounds cover a wide variety of frequencies and in consequence, quick and accurate responses indicated that that particular child was hearing well throughout that range with that hearing aid.

With profoundly deaf children, however, no amount of amplification can make the consonants [s and ʃ] become audible to them, so the test becomes the 3 sound test of hearing, rather than the 5 sound test. Provided parents and teachers know that these high frequency low intensity sounds are not to be included, neither they, nor the deafest children will become frustrated.

Secondly, and perhaps the best possible way, is if the children can be given *pleasurable listening experiences* through the aids. Statements like the following which refer to three partially hearing children who had been recently given aids show that they were convinced of their value.

A boy aged fourteen years with a hearing loss of 45 dB said, "I wore my hearing aid in the park and for the first time I heard the birds whistle".

"In the movies I can hear much better and it will not take long for me to make out every word they say."

A girl aged fifteen years with a hearing loss of 40 dB - "Hearing much better with it. My voice dropped lower. It's better for people who speak to me".

A ten-year old girl with a hearing loss of 53 dB whose mother wrote, "Asked on the first day, 'Is it really necessary for me to wear it, as I can hear just as well without it?'. On the second day, 'If I turn the volume up it whistles - if I turn it up only a little it makes no difference'".On Day 3, "Arrived home all smiles saying 'It *does* make a difference'".

It seemed that at one stage during the third day this girl had perhaps been listening to her teacher and realised she was understanding what was being said better than ever before.

An eight year old girl with a hearing loss of 80 dB said when I visited her home recently, "Wait a minute. I am deaf", and went off to get her hearing aid.

Similarly, statements by very deaf people like Mrs. M. that the hearing aid had "made life more interesting" or of the profoundly deaf Dutch girl who on removing the aid said, "Now I am alone again" are further evidence that the wearers realise that things are better with the aid than without it.

Knowledge About Hearing Aids Can Be Helpful: their performance, the best conditions for using them, the best way to wear them and the general management of them. Ewing and Ewing[45] have given useful suggestions in this connection (*Ibid*, Chapter 13).

The *need for hearing aids* should be created. It is clear that if children are in residential schools where the free use of signs and gestures accompany their almost silent lip movements they do not feel the need for using what hearing they have since they can understand one another, and many of their teachers, quite adequately without the use of sound.

Many teachers have observed that when children begin attending regular (ordinary) schools, that they suddenly become very conscious of the need to obtain as much benefit as possible from their hearing aids and report breakdowns very promptly. Yater (1980),[156] Dale (1984), Schildroth and Karchmer (1986). (The better use of hearing aids thus becomes one more reason why most deaf children should spend as much time as possible surrounded by those who hear normally.)

Integrating with talking people is one good way to show deaf children the advantages of wearing aids, but teachers and parents should see that opportunities arise as often as possible for the children to use what hearing they have - visits to orchestras, to short concerts, to films. to car races, to farmyards, etc., should all be more interesting and meaningful to most deaf children if they are wearing aids (and the aid is working properly!). The children's attention should also, of course, be directed to meaningful sounds in their everyday environment - the radio or television, noises made when preparing food, cleaning the house, at meal times, when gardening or working with tools outside and cars, trucks and motorcycles as they go past.

Finally, with older children who definitely do hear speech better aided than unaided, it is often possible to emphasise to them that in addition to it being easier for them to understand speakers it is easier for the people who talk to them if they wear aids. One can tell such children that people get tired of saying everything to them two or three times over, and that it is so much easier and nicer if one can talk more normally to them.

It should be remembered however, that although older children can set their hearing aid output levels with great accuracy (See Fig. 7:2), many children before the age of 5 years and sometimes considerably later, will accept outputs which are far in *excess* of their most comfortable listening levels. In consequence, many of these unfortunate little children may be dutifully clapping their hands or tapping their table tops and then wearing hearing aids all day which are delivering levels of sound which the same children would not tolerate for a moment when they have become older.

Parents and Supervisors must also be given instruction in the use of hearing aids. The greater their knowledge of the subject the better. Principals and the class teachers have a responsibility here to ensure that such information is given to them. In addition to a certain amount of theory, both the parents and "substitute parents" need to be given demonstrations of what each child is able to hear, with, and without, his or her hearing aid, and they should be able to check the performance of a hearing aid and do the elementary maintenance.

They should also know the best setting for each child's volume controls. Parents should appreciate that during the holidays the sole responsibility for the child wearing his/her hearing aid rests with them.

Residential care of young deaf children has become much less common as specialist visiting teachers have become available to help parents and the possibility of enrolling these young children in regular (ordinary) nursery schools and kindergartens has become more generally accepted.

Where such little children are kept in residential schools over each weekend, it is common for hearing aids to be taken from them on Friday afternoon and returned on Monday morning. This is unfortunate, but is sometimes the only practical and economically feasible practice possible.

When children go home at weekends many schools ensure that they have a supply of batteries and parents have access to cords and receivers if these are required.

Parents should also have the phone number of the technician who is responsible for their child's aid during term time and particularly during vacations.

Supervisors are best to check the hearing aids of the little children at night, (a) to see that they are working, and (b) to ensure that they have been switched off. It is unwise to leave the hearing aids of these young children beside their beds, since they find them interesting playthings when they wake early. Aids should be placed out of sight and reach, each night, and distributed each morning.

In conclusion, then, it is re-emphasised that the more interest that is shown in the hearing aids, the more likelihood there is of a child using them sensibly at all times.

Child Interest and Participation: the aim is that, as soon as possible, the children will become intelligent and discriminating users of hearing aids. They should report faults in the aids as soon as they occur, though very deaf children often have difficulty in doing this. If encouraged, they will inform parents and teachers of the various things they can hear when wearing the aid. As they become older they should be capable of looking after the hearing aid by themselves.

Whilst bearing in mind that to begin with at least, a hearing aid is often something that a deaf child *needs* but doesn't *want*, there are several ways that have proved very helpful in showing them that the aid is of benefit to them, and in consequence to convince them of the value of wearing it. The first is by means of speech tests. For example, if a boy hears 60 per cent of the words in a word list correctly, when using the aid, and only 30 per cent without it, one can show him the scores and say, "You see the hearing aid is useful, isn't it?". Similarly, with profoundly deaf children after using the 10, 5 and/or paired vowel discrimination test, they can appreciate that they *do* have some useful hearing for speech with the aid but cannot even hear the sound of voice unaided. With older children, this semi-scientific approach has often proved a good one.

Personal Paging Systems: severely deaf children (and adults), have difficulty in detecting and responding to such everyday warning sounds as ringing door bells; parents or siblings calling from another room; babies when they cry; calls from a distance when out of doors and also the warning sound of a smoke alarm system.

Fig. 10:1

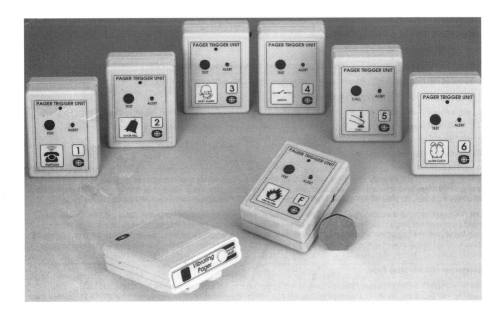

Successful devices for assisting in the above situations have been the development of personal paging systems (PPSs). In Fig. 10:1, a small vibrating "pager" which is worn by the deaf child or adult, is shown in the foreground. Seven different "triggers" are shown at the back of the illustration. One trigger comes into action when the doorbell is rung. The PPS vibrates to alert the wearer who quickly checks which light has come on and, of course, takes the appropriate action. Trigger unit No.2, is able to indicate that the telephone is ringing and where a very deaf person requires to respond, the teletypewriter may be used. (More and more of these ingenious devices are being used throughout the world and have enabled deaf people to make regular use of telegraphic communication). Unit 3 is for doorbells; Unit 4 for responding to a baby's crying and Unit 6 contains an alarm clock mechanism which activates the wearer's vibrator pager at the time desired.

The maker of one PPS has stated "The PPS is battery powered and has a range of coverage exceeding the typical house and garden and is very easy to install". The perception of sound by profoundly deaf children was investigated by Van Uden[146]. It was found that the loud sounds were perceived not only auditorily but also kinaesthetically. In the main, sounds above 500 Hz were *heard*, but sounds below this frequency were first detected as a *vibration in the chest or legs*.

The Ewings[50] described an auditory approach in assisting children to read, speak and, to comprehend language as well as to hear - *(the listening-reading-speaking method or LRS)*. Essentially, it depends on the parent or teacher first speaking close to the microphone of the hearing aid while pointing in a book to each syllable of each word, e.g., "mother" would be tapped twice and "Umbrella" would receive 3 taps as each word was said for the child (or children).

Next, the child is asked to repeat the phrase or sentence while the teacher again points to the words. Success was claimed for this method when only ten minutes of individual practice was given daily. Further evidence supporting this was provided by John and Howarth[88] in a more recent research using this technique with twenty-nine severely and profoundly deaf children. A 56 percent improvement in speech intelligibility was achieved by getting the children to reproduce the teacher's pattern as nearly as possible. The children concentrated on whatever auditory information they could perceive while watching as the teacher pointed to each *syllable*.

In an increasing number of classes and homes in the British Isles today, a similar technique is being used in both group and individualised situations by both parents and teachers of deaf children (Figs. 10:2 and 10:3).

Appropriate language material is written on the blackboard or overhead projector (or in the home/school notebook) and the teacher or parent, speaking close to the microphone of the group or individual hearing aid (or speech training hearing aid) first reads the material right through at a near normal rate. He/she indicates with a pointer or pencil which syllable of each word is being said and the deaf child watches the pointer/pencil as this is done, i.e., the child is encouraged to "watch and listen" as this first reading is completed.

Fig. 10:2

Fig. 10:3

Next the children are taken through the passage again and the meanings of each section are discussed in the conventional way that teachers teach deaf children language, e.g., pictures, apparatus and dramatisation are all used as required to make the meaning clear. The written form of language (although not always exact phonically - e.g. in words such as 'eight', 'foreign', 'know', 'sure' etc.) in most cases gives a much more accurate picture of a word or phrase than either the lipread or signed version of it. It is also, of course, able to be viewed and considered for a much longer period if necessary than either spoken or signed language. For this reason, explanatory words and sketches can usefully be placed between the lines (in a different coloured chalk or ink). As a lesson develops, teachers frequently cover their lips to emphasise that the children must concentrate on the auditory aspects of the language being used. With practice, it is quite remarkable how even profoundly deaf (100 dB) children are able to follow a passage as it is read even though the speech signals they are receiving are only a fraction of those received by normally hearing people. During this "reading for meaning" session, the teacher (or parent) is careful to help the children by tapping each syllable of each word (as emphasised above).

MUSIC FOR DEAF CHILDREN

Music can be perceived by deaf children; they can derive tremendous pleasure from it; and the educational implications of it are considerable. For this reason no publication on the use of sound by deaf children would be complete without reference to music. It is generally known that hearing for the low pitched tones is usually better than for the higher ones. Nearly all deaf children, for example, have measurable hearing at 250 Hz, and below this frequency. Very many have hearing also up to 500 Hz. Middle C on the piano has a fundamental frequency of 256 Hz. The C below this has a main frequency of 128 Hz, and the one above middle C of 512 Hz. It is seen then, that the melodies of many tunes are able to be heard by very many "deaf" people, provided they are produced loudly enough (See Fig. 4:1).

It is important to stress that although the melody can often be heard quite clearly, the harmonics can not - similarly the voice of the singer can be clearly heard but the words he or she sings can never by intelligible to these very deaf children. It is interesting to listen to speech or to singing when the high frequency sounds have been cut out, i.e., low pass filters have been incorporated in the speech circuit at, say 500 Hz. The vowels are all quite audible, but all sound rather like [a] or [u], and the consonants, if they are audible at all, sound like an indefinite breathy type of fricative. The voice takes on much of the quality of a deaf person's speech, except that there is more pitch modulation. Hudgins and Numbers[79] found that the vowel sounds produced by deaf children all tended towards the neutral [a] as in fath*er*. We are reminded once again that "we speak very largely as we hear".

Presenting the Sound of Music to Deaf Children
For children with less severe hearing losses - say up to 70 dB - it seems possible to use very similar methods to those employed with normally hearing children. They are able to sing in a group, to play a variety of instruments and so on. It is very necessary, of course, that they wear their hearing aids for this.

For the severely and profoundly deaf children, instruments like recorders and pianos have been found not to produce the most audible sounds - the recorders seem too weak and the notes on the piano when struck, do not perseverate long enough. Some pianos seem better than others. The children stand round and feel the vibration by touching it. Unless some amplification is used, however, the deaf children are not able to hear the piano music so well (when a note is struck on a piano, the sound very soon drops in amplification whereas the sound on an organ persists much more loudly while an organ note is played). Easily the best instrument for deaf children to hear is the organ. Organs are made, of course, in a variety of shapes and sizes. The one shown in Fig. 10:4 is a wind instrument produced in Holland after much experimentation in the early 1950's.

Fig. 10:4

The specifications were given by Dr. A. van Uden while at the Instituut voor Doven, St. Michiels Gestel, Holland. He became a world authority on music for very deaf children.

One objection to this type of organ is that it is not possible to include the octaves below middle C because the lower reeds become increasingly difficult to vibrate. As Dr. van Uden wrote to the writer many years ago, "The lower the tone, the harder the blow!" This is unfortunate since the children usually hear this range well. If using an electronic organ rather than a wind one, it is, of course, possible to use the lowest notes, but the children then do not have the practice of blowing and exercising the breath control which van Uden and others considered very valuable.

Fig. 10:5

In Scotland recently, it was encouraging recently to see 3 profoundly deaf children combining with 18 normally hearing class-mates as their music specialist teacher conducted them through their first *"orchestral performance"*. These young teenaged boys and girls had become quite "immersed" in playing instruments which included piano keyboards, drum, xylophones and guitars. Group music sessions have the advantage over individual ones that mistakes (which inevitably occur in the early stages), can be "covered up" by the remainder of the group. Each child was able to take a turn at playing any of the instruments he or she chose. The teacher of the deaf children gave what assistance she could - mainly in interpreting what the music teacher suggested to the deaf children as she came around to check how each child was coping.

The John Tracy Clinic has suggestions for parents of preschool children where games and activities can be used to give maximum auditory experience. In Great Britain, the National Deaf Children's Society has suggestions and literature for parents on bringing up deaf children (See Appendix 8:1). Recently some excellent *captioned videotape recordings* have become available that can be ideal for providing interesting auditory experiences for children of all ages. They cost between £20 and £40 (say $30 and $60) and schools and classes can gradually build up libraries of them. These videotapes can be lent to responsible parents when necessary. (One address in the UK is Forest Bookshop, Coleford, Kent). In the USA, parents might begin by writing to the Alexander Graham Bell Association in Washington, D.C. or to their local school or class for deaf children or to their local ordinary primary or secondary (high) school or Department of Education for suggestions about enabling their children to join a class of normally hearing children for some such musical experiences within a group of local children.

It is not essential of course, to have the equipment exactly like that which has been described. Three loudspeakers placed at the back of the stage will give quite a good effect. Two large speakers set in wooden cabinets have proved quite effective in a small room.

A bass-voiced singer with organ accompaniment seems to be one of the best combinations for presenting music to children with defective hearing. This can be tape recorded and played through amplifying systems such as those described above as well as through induction loops.

USE OF THE AMPLIFYING EQUIPMENT

Combining the hearing impaired children with normally hearing ones can often be excellent.

With the nursery and infant groups, the emphasis is on the enjoyment of experiencing sound and developing an awareness to it by activities and exercises that involve hearing and feeling vibrations. Activity methods are used as much as possible, and perhaps 30 per cent of any lesson is devoted to developing physical skills and rhythmical movement where sound perception is not particularly stressed.

1. Children removed their head sets, and went to sit on or under the loudspeakers - shoes removed and individual aids put on.

2. Teacher demonstrated sitting on a chair with feet extended, then kicking rapidly in time with a series of middle C notes played on the Hohner organ.

3. After demonstration by the teacher, children began striding to each not sounded through the loudspeakers - doh Pause doh Pause, etc. At a continuous note, all ran back to the bench. Repeated.

4. Repeated individually or in pairs - the teachers taking note which children were having difficulty. There were only three children of the twelve who seemed at all uncertain.

5.   In a circle - striding around to doh, Pause, doh, Pause, etc. Changed to galloping when music changed to doh-doh, doh-doh, doh-doh, etc. Stopped when the music stopped. Repeated several times. At continuous sound, ran to the seat bench once more.

6.   Lesson ended with physical education activities, climbing on wall bars and forward and backward rolls on a gym-mat. Allocation of time: 1. Wind organs approximately ten minutes; 2. Loud speakers approximately ten minutes; 3. Physical education approximately ten minutes.

It will be noted that the approach adopted when the loudspeakers were used is very similar to that which is used in many nursery schools where rhythmic work is done - i.e., identification of various rhythms; walking, skipping, running, galloping, etc. The only difference, however, is that by using the loudspeakers as well as the induction coil, the children are able to perceive the music so much more clearly than when only a piano or a tape recorder is used.

With older children, the emphasis is placed on finer discriminations of pitch, rhythm, and the length of notes, words and phrases, and a more subtle application of this in speech, in ballet and interpretative dancing.

One period each week was spent playing the wind instruments, and the second period was devoted to dancing. Variety of presentation of material heightens the interest and enjoyment of the work. The following is one way in which a "play song" was presented with 10 year old children over several weeks.

1.   The words of the song were taught in class as a language lesson (and revised again by the specialist music teacher).

2.   The words were practiced in speech periods by the class teacher. One of the methods adopted for speech work in the senior school may be summarised as follows: (a) words are written under a blank staff; (b) syllables are marked; (c) approximate pitches of syllables are marked; (d) syllabic length is shown by musical notation.,

3.   Play on the wind instruments

4.   Compare this pattern with the music of the song

5.   Play the music of the song several times on the wind organ

6.   Revise speech in class

7.   Revision of the tune - played from a tape recorder through both the bank of speakers and the low frequency speaker - children listening and feeling the tunes while they watch the specialist teacher point to the different notes.

8. Language is again discussed and from each phrase the actions of the dance are built up. The movements are a combination of conventional ballet steps and of interpretative dancing, which the children love to devise for themselves.

At secondary (high) school level, several deaf children, assisted by a teacher of the deaf (or sometimes a competent teachers' aide) have been observed frequently participating wholeheartedly in playing a variety of musical instruments. Keyboards, drums, flutes, tambourines and xylophones are shared with their normally hearing classmates.

Music sessions often begin by the children selecting the instrument they wish to play that day and "free play" is allowed for the first 15 or 20 minutes. During this time, the music teacher moves from group to group helping individual children. When she is satisfied that each group is reasonably competent, a simple piece of music is played together. The teacher perhaps playing the piano and conducting.

Although concentration is required, the teacher works quite slowly through the piece of music at first and it is clear that all the children can enjoy the experience a great deal.

Traditional country dancing is also popular in most schools and is certainly popular where deaf and normally hearing children are taught together. In Scotland, children enjoy Highland dancing (See Fig. 10:6). This is especially true if they can be accompanied by a Scottish piper! (See Fig. 10:7).

Fig. 10:6

Fig. 10:7

While the value to children of music and free rhythmical movement are self evident, the work has other extremely important aspects. Learning the words of the songs and pieces is good practice for reading, extends the children's vocabularies and their interest and knowledge of other people and countries. The words also provide interesting and useful material for speech improvement work. Making up play-songs and participating in them is great fun for deaf children and is very good psychologically for them. Many of the songs, nursery rhymes, dances and stories they deal with will be known to their parents and their normally hearing brothers and sisters. These musical activities give excellent opportunities for them to express emotions and ideas in mime, when many of them have considerable difficulty to do this in words. Joy and grief, anger and compassion, weariness and energy, etc., can all be expressed so easily and subtly.

Finally, the use of musical notation to show length (which is of course closely related to strength) of the various syllables, and to help in pitch modulation is most effective when practice is given regularly. If the children hear the words played over first, each syllable being given its correct length, it can have a marked effect on the rate of their utterance and the phrasing and rhythm of their own speech, which makes for greater intelligibility, (See also Appendix 2.5).

Endnotes

In addition to government Departments of Health, Education and Welfare, many organisations have developed privately to assist parents, teachers and others who have been interested in helping deaf children and adults e.g.

United States of America

The Volta Bureau
Alexander Graham Bell Association
3417 Volta Place NW
Washington DC 20007   *(Journal: "The Volta Review")*

The John Tracy Clinic
805 West Adams Blvd.
Los Angeles
California 9007   *(John Tracy Correspondence Course)*

The Rochester Institute of
 Technology for the Deaf
Lyndon Baines Johnson Building
52 Lomb Memorial Drive
Rochester
New York 14623-5604

The Marion Downs Centre for Infant Hearing
Boulder
Colorado 80309-0409

Gallaudet University
Kendall Green
800 Florida Ave. NE
Washington DC 20002-3695

(Regional facilities could be found through local branches of the Department of HEW or possibly the above organisations.)

United Kingdom

The National Deaf Children's Society
National Office
15 Dufferin Street
London EC1Y 8PD   *(Publication: Talk Magazine)*

The British Association of Teachers   Address from current issue of Journal:
 of the Deaf   "The Teacher of the Deaf"

The British Society of Audiology
80 Brighton Road
Reading
Berks   *(Journal: The Journal of the*
England   *British Society of Audiology)*

The Royal National Institute for the Deaf
19-23 Featherstone Street
London EC1Y 8SL
England

The RNID Library
Institute of Laryngology and Otology
The University of London
330 Gray's Inn Road
London WC1X 8DA
England

Chapter 11

COCHLEAR IMPLANTS

Since the early 1960's there has been an increasing interest throughout the Western World in bypassing the impaired cochlear region of the inner ear electronically and thereby stimulating the auditory nerve and the auditory centre of the brain direct. From 1992, the most popular instrument for implantation was the one designed by Professor Graeme Clark and colleagues at the University of Melbourne in Australia (See Figs. 11:1, 11:2 and 11:3).

> *Cohen and Gordon have said the "Cochlear implants are complex electronic devices designed to bypass the defective inner ear and to stimulate remaining components of the auditory nerve in order to restore some sense of hearing. These exciting devices represent the first instance in which technology has been able to restore a meaningful degree of function to a lost sense organ."* *

These writers have indicated that Benjamin Franklin in 1751 appeared to have been the first to suggest that electricity could produce the sensation of hearing. Some 40 years later, Alessandro Volta "boldly tried what no man had tried before" and placed 2 metal rods in his ears before connecting them to a source of electricity! His first reaction was "of a blow to the head" and next that of "the sound of bubbling liquid" before he finally lost consciousness.[†]

To two French doctors, Djourno and Eyries, must go the credit for the first direct electrical stimulation of the cochlear. in 1957 a copper electrode was placed on the auditory nerve of a 50 year old patient while he was undergoing surgery for a chronic ear complaint. This patient was later able to differentiate among different words by hearing alone and noted an improvement in his ability to lipread.

In the U.S.A., Dr. William House in Los Angeles, has been responsible for much of the pioneering work in single channel cochlear implanting. While collaborating with engineer, J. Urban, House performed numerous cochlear implants during the late 1960's. doctors Simmons in Los Angeles and Michaelson in San Francisco respectively, introduced multichannel electrodes after 1964 and during the 1970's professor Graeme Clark and his team of otologists and physicists at the University of Melbourne School of Medicine in

---

* J.L.O. 15 1 1994

† Volta's later work in the field of electroacoustics, however, so impressed Alexander Graham Bell that the AG Bell Association in Washington was named The Volta Bureau and their journal, The Volta Review. (See Simmons, A. - Arch. Otolaryng. 84 24 - 76 1996

Australia, developed the prototype of the multichannel (22 electrode) intracochlear device which became the most widely used cochlear implant in the world in 1990's.

The 22 channel intracochlear implant was approved for funding by the United States government in 1985 and a smaller "Mini 22" implant was approved for use by children down to 2 years of age in 1990. Approval has now been given for application of cochlear implants to children 18 months and older on a research basis.

By 1992, 3,700 adults and 1700 children and teenagers worldwide had the Nucleus Mini System 22 Implant fitted. This system includes;

A. The cochlear implant (See Figs. 11:2 and 11:3)

B. The speech processor. This selects and codes the sounds most useful for understanding speech. (Fig. 11:1)

C. A directional microphone fitted behind the ear and looking rather like a small post aural hearing aid. (Fig. 11:1)

D. The transmitter coil and cable which is held firmly in place over the internal receiver by 2 magnets - one located under the skin and the other in the centre of the external transmitter. (Figs 11:1 and 11:2)

The Nucleus Mini System 22 works briefly, as follows:

1. Sound enters the microphone.

2. It passes as an electrical current to the speech processor.

3. The processor selects and codes the elements that are most useful for understanding speech.

4. These electronic codes are sent back and up to the transmitter ring, which transmits them across to the receiver under the skin.

5. The receiver converts the code to special electronic signals that are passed along the electrode array. (The electrode array is a set of 22 tiny electrode bands - see Fig. 11:3.) These are arranged in a row around a piece of tapered flexible silicone tubing which is placed in the cochlear by the surgeons. Each electrode has a wire connecting it to the receiver.

6.   The coded electronic signals are sent to specific electrodes, each of which has been separately programmed to deliver sounds (which vary in intensity and frequency) to the brain.

7.   The brain interprets these signals and the wearer of the implant thus experiences the sensation of hearing.

As with all new developments, controversy about implants has been fairly widespread. The cost of these operations has been frequently raised as an objection especially when a government department is asked to fund them, so denying other children whose deafness is not of cochlear origin the right to smaller classes, the best hearing aids, etc.

Some adult deaf people, too, have criticised implants on the grounds that they are removing these children from the "deaf culture". Many parents of deaf children, of course, have said "... and a good thing too !", i.e., whilst not having any but the most heartfelt sympathy for those who suffer from profound deafness, they feel that they could "sell their own home" if that could lift the burden of deafness from their child. (There are of course, numerous other ways of raising the necessary funds: street appeals by school children; dances run in schools; door-to-door canvassing by large groups of college students, help from National lotteries as well as assistance from many top surgeons who have given their professional services free of charge to operate on deaf children, etc. See Appendix 11.1).

Fig. 11:1
External Apparatus

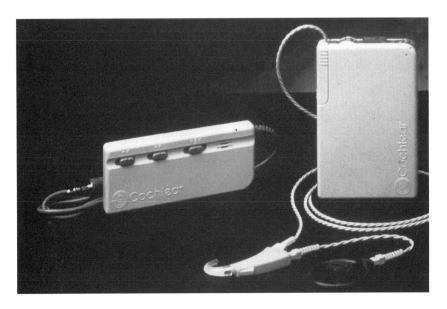

Fig. 11:2
Nucleus 22 channel implant

The elliptical main body of the device has an aerial near its outer edge which activates the circular decoder which then activates the tapering bundle of 22 electrodes. A small circular magnet holds the external transmitting aerial in place.

Fig. 11:3
22 electrodes in place within a dissected cochlear

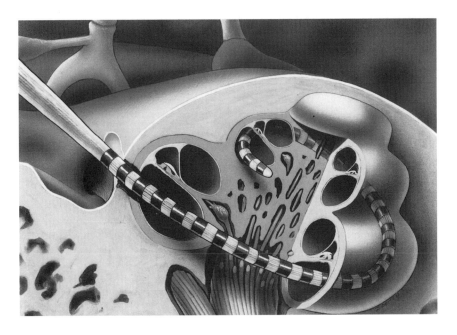

It is significant that although the number of cochlear implant operations performed internationally was fewer than 100 per annum in 1977, by 1988 they had increased to over 3,000 and this number had increased to 14,000 by 1996 (See below). Due to the difficulty of working with prelingually deafened children, however, it is only recently that they have been brought into cochlear implant programmes. It is much easier for example, for an adventitiously deafened adult to inform an implant surgeon precisely what can be heard after an operation - compared with his/her auditory reception prior to the operation or the onset of deafness. It is hoped that some of the speech reception tests of hearing described earlier in this book will prove useful in ascertaining the effect of pre and post-operative hearing for speech with profoundly deaf children.

In January, 1990, 263 children throughout the word had received the Nucleus 22 Channel Cochlear Implant System[124]. Staller, et al. reported that 80 children had worn this device for over 12 months. Their mean age was 9 years and 10 months (age range 2-17 years) and 55 percent of these children were *prelingually deaf*.* Meningitis was the cause of deafness in 49 per cent of these cases and the aetiology was unknown in another 39 percent. The mean age of onset of deafness was 2 years and 8 months.

Pre-implantation thresholds were recorded as 75 dB SPL at 250 and 800 Hz and 95 dB at 1,000 Hz. The thresholds for 2,000 Hz and above, exceeded the limit of the audiometer used. Post-implementation, however, the median thresholds from 250 to 4,000 Hz ranged from 48 to 58 dB SPL.

A little later, Kyeton and Balkany of Yale University, were able to report that:

1. Over 500 profoundly deaf children aged 2-17 years, had been implanted with single or multi-channel cochlear implants during the previous 10 years.

2. Extensive auditory, speech, educational and psychological testing had been performed before and after implantation.

3. Results showed that the cochlear implant provided auditory detection over much of the speech signal.

4. There had been a significant improvement in both auditory discrimination and speech production skills.

5. Limited open set word and sentence recognition had been achieved by at least some of the children.

---

* Had become deaf prior to learning to speak or develop any language

6. The ability to understand speech without lip reading was the ultimate benefit of the cochlear implant. This ability was present in some of the children with sufficient cognition and language skills to take the tests and comparison of speech production skills before and after implantation indicated that speech production improved significantly after implant use.

In 1991, 30 cochlear implant centres had been established in the United States which were staffed by experienced workers. The experts warned, however, that cochlear implant operations should be considered only in centres that could provide the necessary medical, auditory, educational and psychological care for each patient.[†]

Following the U.S. National Institute of Health Conference on cochlear implants in May 1988, one of the final statements of the panel of nationally recognised scientists, offered this timely advice:

> *Children with implants still must be regarded as hearing impaired, even with improved detection thresholds in the range of conversational speech. These children will continue to require educational, audiological, speech and language support services for long periods of time.*

In May 1990, a New Zealand patient apologised for telephoning a cochlear implant surgeon at his home but explained that after 20 years of silence (due to severe meningitis at the age of 18), she was now able to use the telephone again and wished to thank him fervently. Inevitably, as this work progresses, implants will be performed widely on many profoundly deaf children whose deafness is of cochlear origin - which is indeed encouraging.

Clark, et al. (1984)[30] and House (1982) reported that cochlear implant operations were not difficult to perform technically. Although he agreed with this, Ito (1993) reported that he and his colleagues had nevertheless found difficulties when attempting this operation with four of their 21 patients. He felt that problems such as the electrode slipping out of the cochlear or bending in the basal turn or being inserted into a hypotympanic cell by mistake, could certainly occur and in consequence recommended that a radiograph should be taken routinely *"to confirm accurate location of the electrode in the cochlear ... and fixation of the receiver in the temporal bone"*. If an error was suspected, the electrode could then be removed and reinserted.

By 1993 Osberger, Maso and Leslie[113] were able to study 27 subjects with profound deafness who had received single or multichannel cochlear implants. Those who had been fitted with implants early in life had achieved the greatest

---

[†] An excellent editorial on the ethics of cochlear implants for young children appeared in the American Journal of Otology in January 1994, and has been published in full as Appendix 11.1 in this text with the kind permission of Professor N.L. Cohen, M.D.

speech intelligibility. Those not fitted until after 10 years of age had the least intelligible speech.

These writers reported also that although the speech of children who had had later onset of deafness, deteriorated rapidly - their speech intelligibility had improved markedly in most cases, after receiving implants.

When 62 children were evaluated 12 months after the implantation of the Nucleus 22 Channel Cochlear Implant System, 71 per cent recognised one or more words without lipreading. Sixty per cent of the children were able to recognise one or more sentences from a group of ten. The speech of 27 of these 62 children was significantly more intelligible 12 months after implantation than before the operation.[141]

Complications
Kyeton and Balkany's review revealed that during clinical trials with both the multichannel implant and the single channel 3M/House device, the incidence of significant complications had been low (2.4% in the 3M series and 3.5% in the Nucleus series). All of these complications such as infection and extrusion, pain and inflammation and electrode displacement had been successfully resolved. One patient had an unresolved but improved palsy.

Useful comparisons between hearing aided and cochlear implanted children have been made. In once case both groups learned to perceive vowel features before consonants; marked differences in performance were observed between individual children in both groups; both groups were significantly affected by the presence of noise; and finally, implanted children were able to perceive the sound of consonants whereas this was not possible for the hearing aid user group.

It has been emphasised that listening practice sessions should be interesting. Rhythm, rate, intonation and vowel features were all of interest especially when they were presented in games, expressions and activities which seemed more like games than work to the children.

It is also suggested by the writer, however, that once implants are fitted and the post-operative swelling, etc. has settled down, a more suitable place for the child to live is in his/her home and to attend the local ordinary school (after careful arrangements have been made for his/her educational, social and audiological treatment there - See Appendix 1:1). To be surrounded by children and adults who are speaking normally can only be to the child's advantage when he/she is trying to develop such speech and language. DMCD.

Archbold and Robinson in 1997[2] reported the results of their questionnaire survey of 10 cochlear implant centres in the United Kingdom. A total of 388 children had been implanted by the end of 1995; Switzerland; Holland; the United Kingdom and Germany were found to be *largely in favour* of implant programmes by teachers of deaf children; Austria, Belgium, Czechoslovakia and Norway were *neither in favour nor against* and France, Italy, Spain and Sweden were *largely not in favour* of implants for children.*

It became clear in this survey that teachers of the deaf in the United Kingdom were most interested in implant programmes and courses were being established throughout the country where teachers and implant clinic staff could pool their ideas and suggestions for helping these children and their families to be positive yet realistic about assisting implanted children.

A year earlier The British Association of Teaching the Deaf (BATOD), produced their "Code of Practice for teachers of the deaf who worked in implant centres".[7]

Dryden has also made a useful preliminary survey of teachers working with implanted children.[46]

In 1999, Professor Barry McCormick of Nottingham University Hospital, felt able to write a guest editorial for the British Journal of Audiology, entitled 'Paediatric Audiology and Cochlear Implantation in the UK".[99]

In this significant contribution to the literature on implants for young children, McCormick indicated that congenitally deaf children who had been implanted between the ages of 2 and 4 years, had benefited significantly more than those not implanted until 4 to 6 years, "and so on up to the ages of 8 years and beyond when the expectations of success lessen dramatically".[(page 305)]

McCormick continued that since 1991 there had been an "unprecedented escalation in cochlear implants" with nearly 600 children now using implants in the United Kingdom, "this being the number implanted world-wide before 1991".

One in three of the 800 children born deaf in the UK each year would now benefit from implanting. The remaining less handicapped children could be helped by carefully fitted hearing aids and sensitive guidance in their use.

Newly introduced auditory brainstem implants might eventually help a number of those children who are unable to benefit from cochlear implants.

---

* Teachers who are working with children who are using cochlear implants could well subscribe to the network of Educators of Children with Cochlear Implants (NECCI), News, 210 East 64th Street, New York, N.Y. 10021; Fax: (212) 838-6239

Joshua:-

A particularly useful and quite moving article by Taag (1995), described the experience of one couple in Auckland, New Zealand, whose profoundly deaf son, Joshua, had been fitted with a cochlear implant at the age of 2 years. His mother reported that "He breezed through the 4 hour operation and by lunch time that day he was at home playing with (his siblings) and his toys on the floor". A month was allowed before switching on the processor to allow for the swelling to subside and the wounds made, to heal. When the implanted processor was finally switched on, Joshua's mother reported that for *6 months*, they could observe no real response from their son. "Even when I came up behind him and banged pot lids together, he did nothing." The clinic had warned them that it would be a slow process and the mother agreed that it certainly was. Six months later, however, at their seaside house, he suddenly began talking - "What's that?" and "Up, up, up" and "Down, down, down". In fact all the words and phrases that the family had been using with him so conscientiously for all those previous weeks.

Two years after the implant, Joshua (at 4 years old), was speaking in sentences. He was reading very well, could count up to 25; knew all of the colours and was very computer literate. He had become a normal little four year old boy and was a joy to the whole family.

He was going to kindergarten 5 days each week, had speech therapy lessons and loved swimming times at school (especially retrieving 50 cent pieces off the bottom!).

"There is virtually nothing he can't do."

(Scuba diving and contact sports such as rugby or boxing were not recommended, since although the implants are quite robust, a hard blow to the head might, of course, damage them.)

Joshua's mother said that if, when he grows up Joshua wants to meet with other deaf people, he can, of course, do so. At present, however, he most definitely is one who goes forward into the hearing world. "But his parents say, "without the implant he would not have had that choice." (See also Professor Cohen's editorial Appendix 11:1)

"In 1988, only 3,000 implants had been made. By 1995, some 14,000 people worldwide had experienced benefits from cochlear implants." Dr. J.B. Snow, Director of the National Institute of Deafness and other Communication Disorders in Washington, D.C., went on to emphasise that with their 1995 government budget of $168,438,000, major investments were being made in multi channel implants and the support of research to evaluate a new interleaved pulse speech processor. This processor had been tested on cochlear implant patients with encouraging results. "This is one of the most exciting times to be involved in research in human communication." Dr. Snow concluded his article by saying that the NIDCD was pleased to support the search for new ways to prevent, diagnose, treat, and perhaps eliminate disorders of human communication.

A study was reported in 1999 by Bones and Diggory of a 10 year old profoundly deaf child in Derby who had been fitted with an implant at 2.5 years and had developed excellent speech and speech perception skills.[14] In class the teacher used a Connevans 220 FM system and this was shown to be useful to this child. Lipreading was also shown to be of similar assistance in addition to the signal received by the cochlear implant. (Recorded classroom noise was obtained from the Audiology and Education of the Deaf section of Manchester University.)

By the end of a 5 year study of cochlear implantation in the United Kingdom, it was possible for the British Medical Research Council in 1994, to make firm recommendations which have been of immediate assistance to audiologists, parents, teachers of hearing impaired children and to surgeons and medical officers of health (See Appendix 11:2).

From these recommendations, it was clear that provided care was exercised by all concerned, cochlear implanting in the United Kingdom should proceed as soon as implants and expertise became available to each local health district. It was emphasised, of course, that the primary responsibility for optimising cost effectiveness, and being able to demonstrate that such optimisation had been achieved, rested with the providers.

Tactile Aids: Miyamoto, et al (1995) emphasised that there are several sensory aid options for children with profound hearing impairments.[103] Where cochlear implanting is not appropriate, e.g., for financial, religious or medical reasons such as cochlear deformities, tactile aids can represent one valuable option. They are non invasive; they are useful as training devices for children who are awaiting implantation and also following implanting. They have also been found useful as supplements to hearing aids. These writers had, however, found implanted children much more successful in overcoming their communication problems than a control group using tactile only aids (Eilers, et al., 1992).[47]

In conclusion, Miyamoto[103] and his colleagues reported that although many children learned to recognise words and understand speech without lipreading with a multichannel cochlear implant, for others, further investigation into the effectiveness of tactile aids was warranted.

Suggested word lists for Cochlear Implant Cases: For children and young adults who have undergone cochlear implants, much more sensitive speech tests are required. It will be appreciated that with many of these subjects "near normal" hearing ability is aimed for. The two tests described below would be successful for children and young people who had had near normal speech and language prior to becoming profoundly deaf. Where the children's deafness was of long standing, speech tests must be contrived from words which were known to them before the onset of deafness or at least had been learned by them prior to the operation. (*For children whose speech is still defective, each list can be shown to them and they can indicate individual words from each list as they are said to them in random order.*)

Ten Initial Consonant Discriminations
(Senior Students)

1	coat	moat	float	note	goat	throat	boat	gloat	wrote	stoat
2	bed	left	Fred	best	Ned	sped	bless	rest	chest	fed
3	ball	tall	hall	fall	call	stall	brawl	maul	drawl	wall
4	sheep	creep	sleep	deep	steep	sweep	weep	keep	leap	seep
5	pig	dig	jig	twig	rig	fig	wig	gig	zig	big
6	dog	frog	log	hog	jog	bog	fog	cog	grog	clog
7	shoe	new	flew	Sue	stew	crew	Hugh	dew	view	pew
8	boy	toy	coy	joy	noise	Roy	ploy	toys	boys	Roy's
9	bun	gun	fun	sun	run	stun	nun	one	pun	ton
10	car	far	jar	bar	tar	star	ma	pa	scar	dart

Administration

1. Explain to each child that this is a test of *hearing* - i.e., it is not a language test. Say that some of the words (like "gloat" or "stoat" in List 1) may not be known to them but that doesn't matter. "Just point to the word you *think* you heard."

2. Tester reads List 4 pointing to each word as it is said.

3. "Now, (Name), can you find these?" "Sheep; sweep; sleep."

4. "This time *listen* to all of these." Read all of List 4 again, and if the child seems reasonably confident,

5. Administer all 10 lists and record total score as the percent correct. (If a child has difficulty with this test try the Five Consonant test on the next page or some of the much easier speech tests in Chapter 2.)

A Five Initial Consonants Test
(Pictures may be used to assist younger children)

1. coat   boat   note   goat   wrote   *(Practice items)*

2. ball   tall   fall   call   wall

3. sheep   sleep   deep   steep   sweep

4. dog   frog   fog   hog   log

5. bun   sun   run   one   gun

6. hat   cat   rat   mat   bat

Administration

1. Show the words and pictures of list 1 to the child and say *"Watch* and *listen.* Can you show me - 'boat?" If successful, say "Good, now show me 'coat'," etc. until all 5 words have been identified.

2. Next say "Now (child's name), can you show me the words *without watching?"* Hold a sheet of paper over your mouth. Remove the paper while you say "This time, just *listen".*

3. Smile and say the first word with lips concealed. If the child finds it immediately, smile again and go on to another of the words in List 1. If the child makes an error, stop immediately and retrain as in Step 1. above.

4. Finally, administer all 5 remaining list (2-6), and after summing the number heard correctly, multiply the result by 4 to obtain a percentage correct.

5. Any result less than 20% can be disregarded since it would be possible to achieve such a score by chance. Scores in excess of 35%, however, would be significant.

The Nucleus 22 is not the only cochlear implant in use, of course. Other centres in the United States, for example, are using the Med Aid.

An interesting editorial in the BJA (30, 303-307 1997), was able to suggest that the advent of paediatric cochlear implants had revolutionised the medical surgical and audiological management of severely deaf children in those parts of the United Kingdom which were able to take advantage of this new development. Professor Barry McCormick felt able to state that "The routine availability of cochlear implants now enables most very young profoundly and totally deaf children to acquire auditorally based language skills and to function like their severely deaf and moderately deaf peers."

He continued that in his experience, "Degree of success was closely linked with age at implantation and length of time of deafness". Data from the first 100 children implanted in the Nottingham area (which incidentally, had specialised in children below 5 years of age), had shown that 3 years after implantation 87.8% of the children had attained functional spoken language and after 5 years 83% of the children spoke so intelligibly that they could be understood by inexperienced listeners.

The overall results, McCormick considered were very impressive. For the youngest group, however, "they are even more impressive". He observed "The quality of the after-care, including the tuning of the implant and rehabilitation support, contributed very significantly to such high levels of achievement".

It is recognised that not *all* deaf children are able to benefit from implants. Sometimes this is due to their age but there are also factors other than their deafness - social, emotional, psychological or religious - which preclude them from fully taking part in this development.

Professor McCormick concluded his article:- "After years of cautious and gradual route finding, paediatric audiology and the practice of cochlear implantation for the very young are now ideally positioned to take off in the fast lane".

Chapter 12

SCREENING TESTS OF HEARING

At risk registers (sometimes called high risk registers)
At risk groups for hearing impaired children often contain the names of children in an area who have one of the following 10 histories:-
(1) a family history of congenital deafness; (2) cerebral palsy; (3) who were premature (low birth weight); (4) a history of abnormality in the antenatal period, e.g. threatened abortion; virus infection of mother during pregnancy; (5) perinatal abnormality, e.g. asphyxia; Rh. incompatibility (especially kernicterus); (6) who have had a severe illness, e.g. meningitis, or who have been treated with streptomycin for any illness; (7) who are not speaking well be the age of 2 years and between 2-5 years who have speech defects; (8) a history of otitis media and/or chronic upper respiratory tract infection; (9) are not included in any of the above categories but have some congenital abnormality e.g. cranio-facial anomalies; and 10) children whose mothers suspect that their child may not hear properly.

The following useful checklist; the advice about the health visitors and the brief summary have all been abstracted from McCormick's splendid little book *"Screening for hearing impaired children"*[101] with his kind permission. DMCD.

Valuable though *at risk registers* undoubtedly are, it is not infrequently emphasised by experienced medical officers and audiologists that one should also arrange regular screening tests of hearing for *all* the children in an area who are of a particular year of age. Unless this is done, a number of children with significant hearing losses will undoubtedly go undetected.

Infant Screening
Ideally, every child born would have his/her hearing tested during the first few days of life. Such universal testing is known as *screening*, i.e. every child should, so to speak, pass through a screen so that any with significant hearing losses would be identified and given very early medical, audiological and educational assistance to enable them to overcome their hearing handicap as far as is possible.

At a very early age, it is now possible to assess a baby's hearing using otoacoustic emission tests and these are briefly described below.

Otoacoustic Emissions (OAE) Tests

Otoacoustic emissions tests (See Fig. 12:1) are able to measure the sound waves which are emitted from a normal ear when a sound is presented to it while the new born baby sleeps. The stimulus which has been found most useful for this screening test is a very short burst of sound which is described as a "*click*". If no sound is reflected back from the eardrum, an *auditory brainstem response*, (ABR) test is then required, after, of course, a physical examination of the ears has been carried out. Amniotic fluid (i.e., fluid surrounding the foetus), for example, might have been causing the problem.

Fig. 12:1

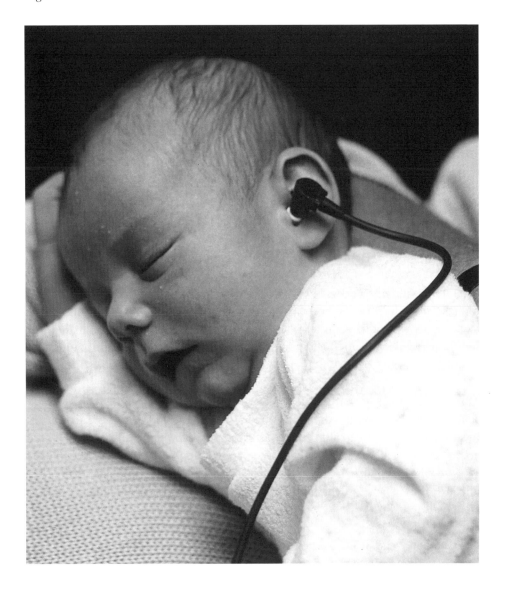

If the ABR showed that there were hearing difficulties a specialist appointment would be made for an audiometric evaluation. In a really efficient screening and follow-up service, the child at this time would be just 3 or 4 days old. Again, ideally, these tests could all be conducted in obstetric hospitals.

(Understandably, mothers frequently wish to return home as soon as possible after the baby is born and where they cannot wait the required 3 or 4 days, tests must be performed at a later date. This is particularly irksome for those living in areas a long distance from specialist facilities. Perhaps parents living in such remote areas should be persuaded to possibly expect a 4 to 5 day stay so that thorough medical and other examinations can be completed prior to their returning home.) See Appendix 12:1 for a very positive development in 17 states of the U.S.A. which is being co-ordinated by Department of Speech, Language and Hearing at the University of Colorado. Soon after some babies are able to sit up on their mother's laps (and certainly after most infants are 7 months old they have been found to be able to turn and locate interesting sounds such as mother's whispered voice or a high pitched rattle, while ignoring less meaningful sounds e.g., an aircraft flying overhead, creating noise levels in excess, say of 90 dB.

From the age of 7 months, little children have been found to turn and locate interesting sounds such as mother's whispered voice or a high pitched rattle, while ignoring the less meaningful sounds.

On subsequent spectrographic analyses, many of the earlier meaningful sounds which were used to test hearing such as crinkling tissue paper, shaking water in a bottle and stirring a spoon in a cup, were found to be composed of a wide range of frequencies. Responses to them, even at very low intensities could not be said to indicate that a child's hearing was normal *throughout the whole speech range*. In the case of a child with Audiogram E in Fig. 4:1, for example, wide frequency noise makers such as the above, would not have indicated that a very severe hearing loss was present in the upper frequencies.

Some of these noise makers are ill used in clinics today for conditioning purposes, but the actual test in most clinics in the United Kingdom now consists of only four meaningful or interesting sound stimuli (see Table 12:1 below).

Conditions Necessary for Test Administration
Screening tests of hearing for babies of 7-9 months of age are usually best arranged in a central clinic *where conditions are quiet*. When screening sessions are conducted skillfully, 25 infants can be tested quite efficiently in one hour. It is heartening that an increasing number of Departments of Health in Developed Countries are offering this service routinely. *Administering screening tests in*

noisy conditions is a waste of time. The testing room should be soundproof. This cannot be overemphasised. It does *not* mean that the room needs to be sound *treated*, which can cost a great deal. Every care should, however, be taken to ensure that rooms used for screening tests of hearing are as quiet as possible. The masking effect of traffic noise for example, can cause children whose hearing is within normal limits spuriously, to appear to have hearing losses of 20 or 30 dB, especially in the low frequencies..

The screening tester should hold a coloured soft toy in his/her hand which can be briefly glimpsed by the child before it is replaced on a bench at the side of the clinic. Workers in Audiology Clinics should not wear white clothes which can, of course, be interpreted by the child as those of a health nurse who may be preparing to offer an injection of some kind.

When testing, the baby should sit upright on mother's lap. The tester should wait until the baby's attention has been gained by an assistant sitting in front of the child and holding an attractive coloured toy as a distractor.

A sound level meter is placed equidistant from the child's ear. See Fig. 2:10, 2:11. The tester stands just behind the child approximately 2 metres away, first on one side and next on the other. Sounds should be produced at the level of the ear under test i.e., the tester should bend down to the correct level. (This again, is important, since pre-school children tend to ignore sounds which occur much above or below their ear level.)

As soon as the baby turns and locates the sound source, the tester smiles and moves out of vision behind the subject and the side and level of sound used is recorded.

If a child fails this test in Britain, he/she is usually re-tested in a week's time. After a second failure the child is referred to his or her school medical officer, health visitor or family doctor with a note regarding the findings. After a routine examination of the ears, nose and throat, more comprehensive and sophisticated diagnostic and perhaps electrophysiological tests may be administered if these are felt to be necessary (See Beagley, H.A., 1981).

When a baby fails to turn to such soft sounds, these are increased by the tester and by positioning a sound level meter (Fig. 2:5) equidistant from the ear being tested (Fig. 2:6) a useful threshold of hearing can be obtained. (In the case of sensorineural deafnesses, the thresholds established in such infant diagnostic tests, frequently match very nearly those obtained some years later when audiometric tests are administered.)

Fig. 12:2

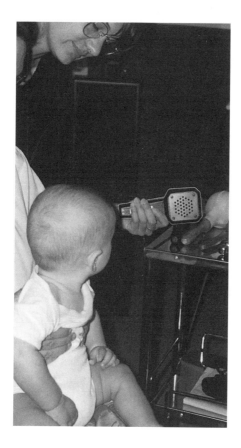

The assistant sitting in front of the baby, records to which side the baby turned; which stimulus noise was used and the level of the stimulus sound.

The most common error in administering these tests, has been that the stimulus sounds are produced too loudly, i.e., the test has become just a distracting test and not a screening test which indicates that the child's hearing is likely to be within normal limits.

A baby who turns to the voiceless [s] sound which has been produced at minimal intensity, for example, has shown good hearing above 4,000 Hz (See Table 5:6 and Fig. 5:6), and this is usually an encouraging sign.

Robson,[123] tested 378 babies aged 9 months, without apparent handicap using meaningful stimuli. She found, however, that not less than 22.8% of these children then failed to respond to even one pure tone when tested with a hand-held audiometer even at maximum intensity (See Fig. 12:2).

Robson concluded that the conventional methods of screening were the most satisfactory, provided, of course, that care was exercised in the administration of same.

Latham and Haggard in 1980 made a study of detecting hearing impairment in the young.[96] Parents were asked:- "Do you think your child is hearing normally? Replies were noted and the "Clues Form" drawn up by McCormick was given to the parents and they were asked to keep it and try to notice if their child's behaviour was similar to that at any time.

After 6 months, a total of 680 records of children were reviewed and the writers concluded that "Parents suspicion of the presence of hearing impairment in their children were found to be reliable and should be sort routinely as indicators in any screening programme". They further concluded that the issuing of the "hints for parents" pamphlet seemed to be the simplest and most efficient technique for unifying a screening programme in a district.

Phonak Ltd, one of the four biggest hearing aid firms in the world, has produced two useful video tapes on *Paediatric Hearing Assessment and Hearing Instrument Fitting*. Their regular paediatric series entitled *Phonak Focus* consists of recently published articles by authorities in audiology. These are supplied to and distributed by this firm's branches in over 70 different countries and are recommended to audiologists, teachers, interested parents and to physicians who work with hearing impaired children.

In an excellent synopsis of the full *"Critical review of neonatal hearing screening in the detection of congenital hearing impairment"* Bamford and Davis[3] emphasised the following points in 1998:-

1. A compelling case for screening all babies born in the UK each year had been made (a) since an estimated 840 children would be born congenitally hearing impaired annually in the UK and (b) late identification, particularly of the more severely impaired children had clearly been shown to lead to poor outcomes in their educational and social development. The writers went on to emphasise that no less than 200 of the 840 hearing impaired children were not identified until after the age o 3.5 years and they suggested that "With no screen in place, the situation would be considerably worse".

2. The neonatal screening service should be supplemented by infant distraction tests at 7 months (particularly for those who had not been screened neonatally). Health visitors, after a one day training period are able to arrange to screen the hearing of 25 seven month old children in one morning session. Two or 3 health visitors can often arrange these mass

screening sessions in one or others; areas.

3.   About 1% of all babies should be audited at random to ensure that the testing was appropriately carried out and that parents were satisfied with the information given, consent sought and procedures.

4.   The person(s) managing the screening programme should be part of the local *Audiology Working Group* whose responsibility was to co-ordinate audiology services and to monitor and implement quality standards*. The NDCS recommended that these groups be in place by the end of 1998.

5.   Davis and Bamford recommended a three group allocation for newborn babies:-
      For full-term babies: transient evoked oto-acoustic emissions (TEOAE) would be assessed as an inpatient. A lack of emissions on either ear would lead to a re-test (still as an inpatient usually but not always immediately after the first test). A lack of emissions on both ears would lead to an automated auditory brainstem response (AABR) test either as an impatient or at recall as an outpatient in 4-6 weeks time. (Where only one ear responds normally, babies are seen again in 6-7 months times.)

      Very early discharge full-term babies: AABR as inpatient (since TEOAE specificity for this group is less than optimal). Lack of response in either one or both ears would be treated as indicated for full term babies above.

      SCBU/NICU babies: AABR or TEOAE as an inpatient; lack of responses on either ear would lead to AABR retest as an inpatient, with unilateral or bilateral failure leading to 'diagnostic' ABR when appropriate.

      The writers indicated that the weight of evidence strongly supported the development of national screening tests for permanent con genital hearing impairment based on universal neonatal hearing screening and this should be supplemented by continued surveillance and the use of distracting tests. This, they felt provided the best value for money and potentially, could offer the greatest benefit to hearing impaired children and their parents and families.

      Davis and Bamford concluded their article (in the British Journal of Auditory 37 1-6 1998) "Britain once led the world" in the introduction of infant screening and in paediatric audiology and quoted Sir Alexander Ewing, 1957 and Doctors Mark Ross and Marion Downs, 1998 who had borne this out.

---

* See National Deaf Children's Society Quality Standards (NDCS) - 1996 Volume.

School Aged Children

In addition to the national screening tests of all children, of a particular year of age, teachers in ordinary (regular) schools are advised to look for the following behaviour which frequently indicates that a child's hearing is not within normal limits:

❖   Continues writing when the class is asked to stop
❖   Misunderstands quite simple instructions
❖   Frequently seeks assistance from a neighbour
❖   Obtains particularly low marks in oral tests although quite satisfactory results are obtained in written work
❖   Appears to watch teacher's lips much more closely than other children
❖   Distracts other children during oral language work (because he/she is unable to understand what the teacher or classfellows are saying).
❖   Achieves much better results in non-verbal intelligence tests than on the verbal scales of the same test.*

Screening Tests of School Aged Children

In developed countries, a national check of each child's hearing is usually carried out when they are 6 years of age. (Any children who are earlier suspected of having difficulties with hearing are, of course, referred to the appropriate school health service and/or to their health visitors audiology clinics and their general practitioners.)

A second national check of school aged children's hearing is often carried out at the age of 13 years when they are beginning their secondary (high) school careers.

When testing the hearing of school aged children, noise excluding earphone shells or covers have been found to attenuate external noise very markedly and these should be used routinely by all those engaged in screening tests in ordinary schools (Fig. 12:3).

For children who fail a screening test, a second test is made a week later and children failing this test are referred by the headteacher to the local audiology clinic or school health service.

J. Robson, medical audiologist for the County of Lancashire (1965-1985), made the useful points that, in addition to ascertaining deafness in children at an early age, screening tests were extremely worthwhile, not only because they made the general public more aware of deafness in children, but also because they had detected large numbers of deaf and partially hearing children with additional other physical and mental conditions requiring attention - e.g., cerebral palsy,

---

* Many teachers, of course, have indicated that a large proportion of their classes in ethnic minority schools or in lower socio-economic areas exhibit most of the above characteristics - although their hearing may be perfectly normal.

mental deficiency and visual defects.*

In the United Kingdom, and parts of United States one day courses have been conducted regularly in audiology clinics for public health nurses in the use of simple but effective distracting tests of hearing for infants.

Noise Excluding Enclosures
When screening tests are administered in many ordinary school situations, the background noise can be such that stimulus sounds must be produced quite loudly before even children with normal hearing are able to perceive. In consequence, large covers must be placed over the headphones of the audiometer to overcome this problem (See Fig. 12.3). The makers have stated that these enclosures not only permit accurate audiometry in conditions of ambient noise too high for conventional audiometer headphones, but also can be easily fitted to audiometer earphones using standard TDH 39 inserts. No change is necessary in the audiometer calibration at the time of fitting. Enclosures are invaluable where no sound-proofed room is available.

Fig. 12:3

---

* Discussion with the writer, October 1994.

The attenuation of noise that can be achieved by using additional earphone covers as shown in Fig. 12:3 are listed in Table 12:1 below.

Table 12:1

Attenuation possible to audiometer headphones by the use of noise excluding earphone covers

Frequency Hz	Attenuation dB
125	9
250	13
500	24
1000	30
1500	32
2000	39
3000	44
4000	44
6000	44
8000	35

Table 12:2

Screening Tests Items for Infants

Low frequencies (below 1,000 Hz)

1. Soft voice in sentences containing approximately 8 syllables, e.g., "Hello Betty. Look what I've got".*
2. A low pitched rattle very gently shaken or alternatively, softly spoken "Boo-boo-boo-boo-boo-boo-boo".

High frequencies (above 4,000 Hz)

3. A high pitched rattle[‡] gently rotated
4. Rhythmic repetition of minimal "s".

If a child fails this test, he/she is re-tested in a week's time. After a second failure the child is referred to his or her school medical officer or family doctor with a note regarding the findings. After a routine examination of the ears, nose and throat, more comprehensive and sophisticated diagnostic and perhaps electrophysiological tests may be administered if these are felt to be necessary (See Beagley, H.A.[9]).

---

‡ A rattle containing small spherical plastic pellets which produces sounds only above 4,000 Hz very effectively. (Obtainable from the Centre for Audiology, and Education of the Deaf, The University, Oxford Road, Manchester 13, England - and doubtless from other sources.)

When a baby fails to turn to such soft sounds, these are increased by the tester and by positioning a sound level meter (Fig. 12:10) equidistant from the ear being tested (Fig. 12:11), a useful threshold of hearing can be obtained. (In the case of nerve deafnesses, the thresholds established in such infant diagnostic tests, frequently match very closely audiometric test results obtained several years later.

The training of staff to conduct screening tests of hearing in every area of every country is an ongoing process. New staff must be continually trained and experienced staff encouraged by informing them of results from other regions and nationally.

A publication by the Director of the National Institutes of Health indicated that in certain regions of the United States much more attention should be addressed to this important topic. After a meeting of some 50 academics and specialists in the early identification of hearing impairment in infants and young children it became clear that in parts of some states far more needed to be done (American Journal of Otology, Vol:15:4, 1994).

(The virtue of the tests described earlier in this chapter, which have evolved over many years, do represent a means of detecting significant hearing losses in the infant and school-aged population both rapidly and inexpensively.)

APPENDICES

APPENDIX 1:1
INDIVIDUALISED MAINSTREAMING
Audiological, Educational, Economic and Social Advantages
(An open letter to Chief Education Officers and Chief Medical Officers)

For over 200 years, the majority of deaf children in developed countries have been educated in special schools. During the past 40 years, special classes for hearing impaired children have developed rapidly in many western countries.

Although these special classes in ordinary schools have often been found more popular with children, parents and teachers than completely segregated special schools, two quite serious problems have frequently occurred with them.

1. *Academic attainments* have remained limited e.g. reading ages, frequently flattening at about 8.5 years and the speech of the deafest children remaining grossly defective.

and

2.   *Socially*, although often accepting the deaf children quite casually, few really close friendships have developed between the two groups of children. On the rare occasions when closer relationships between deaf and normally hearing children *have* occurred, their homes have frequently been several kilometres apart and little contact can be made during after school hours (i.e. deafness is such a rare handicap that children in special schools or units must frequently travel quite long distances to school).

Since 1970 we have been researching the possibility of educating nearly all deaf and partially hearing children *individually* in their own local primary and secondary schools.[34, 35] As a former principal of a school for deaf children, I can say that the results have been quite remarkable and encouraging. Both the deaf and the normally hearing children have been very happy with this new form of special educational treatment. Parents and teachers of the deaf have also been most impressed and convinced of the merit of this new approach. (See also Yater (1977), Schildroth and Karchmer (1986).

In a nutshell, we have found that the correct amount of support for each child is *critically important*. This varies from child to child. For example, young severely deaf children of average or below average intelligence from homes which are not able to be particularly supporting educationally, require a full time welfare assistant and a daily visit from an itinerant teacher of the deaf. Older, less deaf and more gifted children from educationally supporting homes, however, require much less individualised assistance.

Audiologically it has become clear that the amount of speech and language input for each hearing impaired child can be immeasurably greater in a carefully organised mainstream situation. This is provided, of course, a continuous effort is made to ensure it. (See Dale, "Individualised Integration" 1984.)

Adult deaf people, too, are also naturally very apprehensive about such individualised programmes until they see them in action. They then realise that each deaf child is receiving an unprecedented amount of attention through the daily one-to-one verbal contact with his/her welfare assistant, the teacher of the deaf and also from his/her classfellows. (Social clubs for adult deaf people are discussed later.)

A point which should be emphasised here is that *all* the experienced teachers of deaf children who have been involved with me in London since 1970, have been worried in the beginning about placing profoundly deaf children individually in their local ordinary schools. Provided one is careful in one's planning, however, it soon becomes clear that such programmes can be extremely successful and deaf children are much more easy to teach in these situations. They clearly prefer such placement to that of deaf school or unit, frequently saying it is "more interesting".

At infant and primary level, half time or part time welfare assistants are also able to make useful summaries of work covered and points missed by a deaf child at school and these can be taken home to parents and hostel parents in the invaluable *home/school notebook* (See Dale - 1984).

At secondary (high) school, support for the deaf children can come from former ordinary (regular) high school teachers who are employed on an hourly basis and are assisted by the itinerant teacher of the deaf.

This is particularly helpful for specialist subjects such as maths, physics, chemistry or domestic science where some teachers of the deaf may be of little or not help!

The itinerant teachers of the deaf frequently exchange their home telephone numbers with these part time special subject teachers and, of course, with the parents of the deaf child and the welfare assistant.

This individualised assistance for each deaf child is often enjoyed by both the experienced semi-retired teachers and by the deaf children. It is also appreciated by class and form teachers and by the children's parents. (See Dale - 1984, Ross - 1991 and Yater - 1977.) Local Education Authorities can usually fund such programmes when the cost of alternative provision is considered (See below).

In large secondary (high) schools there are often *several* children who wear hearing aids. It is encouraging for them to realise that they are not "the *only* child who needs to wear a hearing aid". They should, however, be given as much individualised assistance as possible in *all* subjects and particularly in those involving a great deal of language.

As well as help from teachers and special welfare assistants, other children can be tremendously helpful and in so doing, can get to know the deaf children much better. It has frequently been observed that many of the friendships which have developed between deaf and hearing children have come about through them having been placed together in classrooms. (Knowing this, a number of schools have even placed children living in the same street as the deaf child, close to him or her so that they may be able to converse more readily out of school hours.)

Some teachers feel that the normally hearing children should concentrate on their *own* work and not be distracted with helping another child. In certain cases this may well be true, but on the positive side, there is an advantage in explaining work to another child - "I listen and I *learn* but I teach and I *understand*". Teachers generally know which children can be asked to take on this extra responsibility and not to ask too much of any particular pupil.

Advisory and itinerant teachers of the deaf, who previously were teaching in deaf schools and units in the other English programmes and in Milan and Bologna, have all made it clear that they have been both surprised and pleased with this new development. Parents have told the writer that their children come home from their local ordinary schools each afternoon, tired, but by no means unhappy. Both the parents and all of the children have assured the headteachers of the deaf schools and the ordinary primary and secondary schools that they are keen that these programmes should continue.

When the Tarra School for Deaf Children in Milan was visited in 1980, it had reduced from an enrollment of 400 to just 32 children as a result of their excellent individualised mainstreaming programme. Both the 21 parents and the 17 teachers met on that occasion assured me of the success of the new approach compared with the traditional method where the children were taught in class groups with the school for the deaf or in the local unit.

There will undoubtedly be a large number of hearing impaired children wearing hearing aids in every country who already attend ordinary schools individually, but not the 80 or 90 percent of hearing aid users who are attending their ordinary schools in large parts of England and in Milan and Bologna.

Costs

The overall cost of this new approach is still expensive when compared with educating normally hearing children, but in 1997, we were able to calculate that it was only half of that of day school for the deaf or special unit classes and only one third that of residential school placement. (See also Dale - 1984.)

Local Education Authorities are usually happy to finance such additional remedial teaching for a deaf child to remain in his/her local ordinary school. This is especially so if they can be convinced that care has been taken in assessing the child's needs and also that the alternative to this extra coaching and support, will be admission to an expensive full or part-time residential school or special unit class.

It will be appreciated that no new buildings are required for individualised programmes, no taxi or special school bus fares to get the children to school as is often the case when groups of children are transported quite long distances to a central school. A huge saving is made on the salaries of all the non-professional staff who are essential to maintain large residential schools. (At the day and residential school for the deaf children of which I was the principal in the early 1960's no less than 40 non-teaching staff were employed to keep the school running effectively. These included gardeners, cooks, secretaries, a handyman-carpenter, a matron and sub-matron, a nurse, 8 lady attendants and 2 housemasters, a seamstress, housemaids and a part-time librarian. Eight teachers also lived in the school free of charge for one afternoon and evening's supervision duty and a further two afternoons' and evening's duty every 8th weekend.)

At the beginning and end of each school term, teachers and supervisors were paid to escort the children to and from the deaf school. (The cost of the children's schooling and residential care, was calculated as being higher than the fees at that time being charged by the exclusive English public schools of Eton or Harrow!)

Once each month, or once each week in some cases, the individually integrated deaf children return to the deaf school or unit class for an hour or so after school on one afternoon. They are then able to renew friendships with their former class fellows and (over a soft drink and biscuit), can chat about their various experiences in their new schools. Parents too, of course, also enjoy these meetings when they are able to to have relaxed discussions with other parents and also the teachers of the deaf and later, the specialist subject teachers and the welfare assistants.

When it was suggested to a group of adult deaf people recently that the deaf children should return to their former school once each month, they all said that once each month between meetings was too long. "Every week!" they said to the writer unanimously. It should be remembered, however, that the adult deaf people had undoubtedly spent many hours in normally hearing society, not able to understand a word of what was being said and doubtless feeling both lonely and uncomfortable. It should also be remembered that in carefully arranged individualised programmes, no child is left alone for long periods and as indicated they usually say that life is more interesting in the individualised mainstream setting.

As the children become older, such meetings usually become oriented towards life after school-days are over. Job prospects, vocational guidance and placement, and tertiary education can become interesting topics of conversation on these occasions.

The purchase of FM hearing aids (Figs. 1:10 and 1:11) is exceptionally useful in these situations. In secondary (high) schools, the hearing impaired child leaves the transmitter section on the teacher's table as he/she enters the classroom, the teacher places the strap over his/her head, looks at the hearing impaired child to check that everything is functioning satisfactorily, and then continues the lesson in the normal way. At the end of the session the teacher simply removes the transmitter and leaves it on the table for the hearing impaired child to take to the next classroom.

When a teacher is repeating a subject in much the same way as was done the previous year, it is often possible to obtain (borrow) exercise books from a child or two children who have kept very neat books the previous year and these can be lent to the hearing impaired child to aid in preparing for lessons, for help during the lesson and for revision after each lesson. One is reminded of profoundly deaf Dr. Marsters' comment to the writer in Los Angeles, that "A deaf child must work as few normally hearing children do if he or she hopes to follow a course designed for unhandicapped children".

Empty rooms in schools for deaf children and those in units, have sometimes been found very useful for all teachers in that area to meet for in-service work and sometimes at centres where everyone can meet for relaxation and general discussion (often on a Friday afternoon).

What of the 10 or 20 percent who are unable to be successfully individually mainstreamed?

Some of them may reside at the school for the deaf where they are cared for 24 hours a day if necessary, by trained staff who are skilled in meeting their special needs.

Some parents living in remote country areas have been able to move their homes so that their child is able to receive the special services required and still return home each afternoon.

In other cases, a local lady who perhaps had previously been a primary school teacher, is happy to act as a teacher-cum-welfare assistant, when the the teacher of the deaf is unable to visit more than once or twice each month.

Services for every child should be carefully reassessed each year and much more frequently in exception cases.

At high school level, some deaf children find it difficult to maintain friendships with normally hearing children and prefer the company of other hearing impaired children out of school time. Teachers and parents should take care to cater for this.

Membership of well run deaf clubs should also be available in cities where deaf people can go to relax together after work and at the end of each week.

Attending ordinary schools and college does not, of course, enable hearing impaired people to overcome their deafness - as cochlear implantation has done in some cases - but it certainly enables more children who previously would have been segregated, to live happily in their normal auditory environment while they are growing up.

APPENDIX 1:2

(Abstracted by kind permission of Hodder and Stoughton, London and Charles C. Thomas Ltd. Springfield, Illinois, from *Individualised Integration*, Chapter 11).

PREDICTIVE FACTORS WHICH ENABLE SUCCESSFUL INTEGRATION

The following list briefly summaries important factors mentioned in the preceding chapters. It is recognised that it is neither possible (nor desirable) for every factor listed to be checked or provided in the case of every child. A reasonable number of these points should be taken into consideration, however, if one is to expect the programme to be successful. As has already been indicated, when an appropriate hearing aid is fitted and ample daily support from an imaginative teacher, parent or welfare assistant is available, many other factors, although still important, become less critically so. Academic ability, age and personality do, of course, also have high predictive value.

It will be appreciated that all these factors vary from child to child and from one year to the next. For example, one child may have an excellent teacher but a home which cannot offer much assistance, another may have the reverse, and a third child may have a good home and an excellent hearing aid but may be slow in learning. The task of those arranging the support for each child is to weigh up these various factors - considering the pros and cons in each child's situation - and then provide the degree of support which seems to be appropriate.

1   Selection

It should be remembered that:

(i)   every child should be considered

(ii)   work for successful placement should begin six months before the child to be individually integrated beings school

(iii) where possible, entry should be at the beginning of the school year rather than halfway through

(iv)   the amount of support required depends on a variety of personal, social, educational and audiological factors. For example, young, profoundly deaf children of low intelligence require continuous support from a welfare assistant, and regular visits from an itinerant teacher of deaf children, but older, bright, partially hearing children can often succeed with the minimum of special educational intervention.

Assessments

The following factors should all be taken into consideration when a child is being considered for individualised integration:

Personal   (1)   Age
               (2)   Hearing loss
               (3)   Academic ability
               (4)   Personality of child
               (5)   Amount of support able to be given in the home

School   (1)   Head teacher
               (2)   Class teacher(s)
               (3)   Remedial teaching available
               (4)   Class size and composition (e.g., number of children with special needs already enrolled)
               (5)   Classroom(s): large or small, acoustics, lighting, possibility of tutoring child in classroom
               (6)   Teaching aids and materials available to the class - hardware and software
               (7)   Preliminary visit with parents and child - check seating, etc.
                     Availability of special assistance

Amount of assistance possible from:
* advisory teacher of deaf children
* itinerant teacher of deaf children
* remedial teacher
* welfare assistant
* home assistant/volunteer*
* parent
* teacher tutoring before or after school
* classmates
* volunteer

Equipment that will be available to the child:
* radio transmitter
* hearing aid(s), make(s) and model(s); earpiece(s), make(s) and no(s)
* speech trainer
* slide viewer
* language master
* textbooks, pictures and other teaching aids

Assistance possible from parents:
* travel to school (busy roads to cross, etc.)

* checking hearing aids
* home/school notebook
* family diary
* membership of local library
* place for child to do homework
* someone to help supervise homework if parents unavailable
* visiting school for meetings (private and public)

2   One week before entry to school

* Administer appropriate educational and social adjustment tests and schedules (See Chapter 10)
* Discuss results, first, briefly with teacher(s) and then in detail after two weeks, when he/she/they know the child better

3   Within one month

* Teacher of deaf, class teacher and child to plan a *brief* lesson on hearing impairment for the child's class
* Micro-teaching unit established if possible. Help select child's friends and acquaintances and again, if possible, from children living near him or her
* Home/school notebook begun if possible
* Child enrolled in local library, accompanied by parent if he/she is unable to do so himself/herself
* Head teacher/head of department and form/class teacher to attend a one-day session on hearing-impaired children at a teachers' college or education center. Medical, audiological, educational, social and emotional data given - generally and specifically
* Parents encouraged and helped to visit the school (head teacher to invite them).
* Occasionally, itinerant teacher to take class while class/form teacher tutors the hearing-impaired child individually (and sometimes with another child who is causing concern).

Reassessments

To be made at the end of Term 1 and during the second half of Term III, to be followed by conferences of relevant personnel: parents, head teacher, advisory teacher, itinerant teacher, class teacher, psychologist, school medical officer and so on.

APPENDIX 2:1

R.N.I.D. HEARING TEST CARDS

Card 1	cup	duck	jug	bus
Card 2	egg	peg	hen	bed
Card 3	cap	fan	cat	lamb
Card 4	key	feet	sheep	tree
Card 5	dog	cot	doll	sock
Card 6	knife	pie	pipe	kite

APPENDIX 2:2

M/J WORDS (SLIGHTLY ADAPTED)

List 1	List 2	List 3	List 4
A. car	F. ship	K. hand	P. look
bird	home	white	feet
school	cup	duck	chair
come	made	bed	road
play	egg	doll	egg
B. duck	G. day	L. car	Q. ship
bed	fish	mice	horse
broom	book	frog	bus
pig	ball	door	cow
doll	shoe	moon	black
C. four	H. horse	M. four	R. cup
shop	night	bird	long
hand	black	mat	day
man	feet	shop	girl
frog	man	play	night
D. sat	I. hat	N. come	S. hat
green	bus	fat	home
door	long	school	boat
white	chair	get	fish
mice	boat	green	shoe
E. cat	J. three	O. gun	T. three
gun	road	pig	jump
brown	girl	wood	man
wet	cow	cat	ball
wood	jump	brown	made

List 5	List 6	List 7	List 8
A. bad	F. book	K. with	P. good
dish	kind	put	room
sleep	train	milk	fast
milk	fast	car	one
boy	good	down	ball
B. run	G. pot	L. bad	Q. pot
fall	floor	fall	kind
house	meat	dog	big
put	dad	bow	train
mine	door	sheep	wash
C. bow	H. give	M. mine	R. dad
bed	ball	sleep	mouse
five	mouse	red	said
with	hair	food	hair
yet	big	house	book
D. sheep	I. room	N. bed	S. give
her	saw	some	cap
down	cap	yes	hen
food	stick	fat	meat
car	three	boy	stick
E. cat	J. hen	O. five	T. door
red	wash	gun	jump
dog	jump	her	three
has	one	cat	saw
gun	said	dish	floor

APPENDIX 2:3

ADAPTED K/T LISTS

List 1	List 2	List 3	List 4	List 5	
knife	fork	gate	duck	horse	
fish	pin	egg	boat	doll	
house	boat	sheep	cat	pig	
car	tree	mat	brick	hen	
brush	shoe	dog	ball	bus	
bus	key	match	cup	dog	
pipe	horse	wheel	pig	egg	
cow	tin	plate	mat	ball	
string	spoon	bed	fork	glove	
bath	*soap*	*watch*	*stone*	*pin*	
chair	cup	shoe	tree	man	Distractors
bird	cat	boat	cow	soap	

183

APPENDIX 2:4

TESTS OF SPEECH PRODUCTION*

Speech production test 1: consonants and rate of utterance
Three characteristics of speech: consonant articulation, rhythm and rate of utterance have been found to be of critical importance in achieving intelligible speech (Hudgins and Numbers 1942[79], Spencer 1970[135] and Subtelny 1979[139]). The first part of this test assesses the child's ability to say 25 consonants in easy words in initial positions, one is medial ('meaSure') and one final ('riNG') - since these last two sounds do not occur in initial positions in English. The other consonants have not been tested medially or finally since this lengthens the test and makes it less practical for teachers. (All the consonants can, of course, be placed in these other positions for testing and teaching whenever the teacher/therapist so desires.)

Another constraint in constructing this test was the need for ease of administration and scoring. (With a little practice, both parts can usually be given and scored in five minutes.)

To be useful and interesting for young children, the material had to be simple and able to be illustrated. Each child can keep a personal test sheet of the words, and most enjoy colouring in the picture after each test sound is able to be pronounced correctly.

Part 1: Consonant Articulation
The aim is to give each child the best possible opportunity to say each test phoneme as intelligibly as possible in a word. The tester sits two or three feet away, in the quietest possible situation. Light should be on the tester's face; for example, he or she should be facing the window. One should speak within four to six inches of the microphone of body-worn or speech-training hearing aids, taking care that the microphone does not conceal the speaker's lips. The test sheet is placed in front of the child; the tester smiles and says: "I want you to say these words" (indicating them) "with good speech". The tester points to the first picture and says: "This is a path". He/she next points to the word: "This says path". "Now" (looking at the child as he or she watches) "Can you say path?" Two more trials are given after the tester repeats the test word. The microphone is passed from the tester to the child on each of the three occasions. If the initial sound is said perfectly by the child on one or more of the three trials, it is scored as correct.

184

Treat the next words of the test in the same way. Multiply scores that are correct by four to obtain percentages.

When 40 per cent or more is achieved on this test, much of the child's speech will be intelligible, even to those unfamiliar with the speech of deaf children.

Fig. 1

path tap car boy door girl mother nine

ring white fish thin sea shoe chair window

van the zebra measure jump lamb run yellow hop

Table 1

Name:_____

	Date:																
	Tester:																
p	path																
t	tap																
k	car																
b	boy																
d	door																
g	girl																
m	mother																
n	nine																
ng	riNG																
wh	white																
f	fish																
th	thin																
s	sea																
sh	shoe																
ch	chair																
w	window																
v	van																
th	the																
z	zebra																
zh	meaSure																
j	jump																
l	lamb																
r	run																
y	yellow																
h	hop																
	Total																
	× 4 = %																
	Rate Trial 1 Trial 2 Trial 3																
	Mean Rate																
	Chronological Age																

NOTE: There is a tendency for testers to be too lenient in scoring this part of the test. It is most important to remember that, unless a sound is said perfectly, it should be marked as an error, i.e. "A good try" is not sufficient. Objectivity is lost if any other criterion is used and results obtained are then of little value.

When used by teachers, results of subsequent tests can be graphed for each child's personal file. As well as being encouraging to both child and teacher/therapist, this information can be of real assistance throughout the day. If, for example, a teacher or parent knows that a particular sound can be produced perfectly on one of three trials, he or she knows whether it is reasonable to encourage its use when the child is speaking on some other occasions during the day.

(In all speech work, it is, of course, important to remember Spencer's homily that "All teaching should be fun". Coercion or continual nagging is usually counterproductive.)

Part 2: Rate of Utterance
The object here is to measure the rate at which the child reads each of these three lists of words when speaking at his or her normal rate.

Show the child a digital watch or the second hand on a wristwatch; indicate the first list of eight words, and say: "Now, I want you to say all these words using good speech and don't gabble". (Demonstrate by saying the first row of eight words in rapid succession.) "But don't go too slowly either." (Demonstrate with exaggeratedly deliberate speech.)

"Ready - go." (Tester moves hand downwards - neither too slowly nor rapidly, i.e., encouraging a normal rate of utterance from the child.)

Record time
After completing all three lists of words, sum the three times recorded at the bottom of the score sheet, divide by three and record the *mean* rate of utterance.

Normal rates for reading these three lists with good speech are:

5-year olds:	8.00 seconds
7-year olds:	7.00 seconds
9-year olds:	6.00 seconds
Adults:	4.5-5.00 seconds

If deaf children speak much more rapidly or more deliberately than this, intelligibility is usually lost.

Vowels and Diphthongs

Due to difficulties involved in assessing the intelligibility of vowel sounds - accent, voice quality, etc. - these have not been incorporated as part of the above test. Seventeen of the 25 words do, however, contain the commoner English vowels and diphthongs and these can be assessed on other occasions.

Testing and scoring (See Table 12) are similar to that indicated above for consonants except that the score for the 17 phonemes correct is multiplied by six to obtain an approximate percentage intelligible for vowels and diphthongs.

Table 2

		DATE										
		TESTER										
Long vowels:	ar	cAR										
	or	doOR										
	ir	gIRl										
	ee	sEA										
	oo	shOE										
Short vowels:	i	wIndow										
	a	vAn										
	ə	zebrƏ										
	u	jUmp										
	e	yEllow										
	o	hOp										
	oo	fOOt (of the runner)										
Diphthongs:	oy	bOy										
	i-e	nInE										
	air	chAIR										
	ow	windOW										
	ear	EAR (on the lamb!)										

APPENDIX 2:5

NATIONAL ACOUSTIC LABORATORIES' ADAPTATION OF THE MRC WORD LISTS

	List No. 1	*List No. 2*	*List No. 3*	*List No. 4*
Practice Items:	1. your	1. glow	1. oat	1. you
	2. touch	2. queer	2. fiend	2. quit
	3. frost	3. mean	3. slim	3. shift
	4. all	4. think	4. our	4. last
	5. pet	5. yawn	5. more	5. reel
Test Items:	6. splash	6. hurl	6. bait	6. solve
	7. lunge	7. thrash	7. suck	7. rear
	8. cleanse	8. dim	8. vast	8. watch
	9. nook	9. crave	9. bean	9. wrath
	10. bad	10. jam	10. job	10. punt
	11. smile	11. ball	11. trash	11. rode
	12. cane	12. lush	12. niece	12. wink
	13. there	13. why	13. pick	13. thud
	14. folk	14. path	14. bad	14. fowls
	15. hive	15. rouse	15. earl	15. choose
	16. toe	16. gnaw	16. need	16. sly
	17. rag	17. wedge	17. five	17. green
	18. grove	18. nest	18. dark	18. true
	19. are	19. please	19. log	19. pipe
	20. dish	20. rate	20. rap	20. kid
	21. is	21. neck	21. scythe	21. bathe
	22. use	22. take	22. mute	22. scare
	23. then	23. muck	23. fate	23. tug
	24. feast	24. wharf	24. frog	24. trade
	25. clove	25. trip	25. choice	25. sick
	26. like	26. sob	26. snuff	26. inch
	27. no	27. air	27. nut	27. roe (or grow)
	28. rub	28. flush	28. sludge	28. add
	29. docks	29. cast	29. blush	29. feed
	30. pants	30. ache	30. pit	30. high

APPENDIX 3:1

AUCKLAND AUDIOMETRIC AND
SPEECH TEST RESULT FORM

A form used to record audiological and speech test results.
(Courtesy National Acoustic Labs., Auckland, New Zealand)

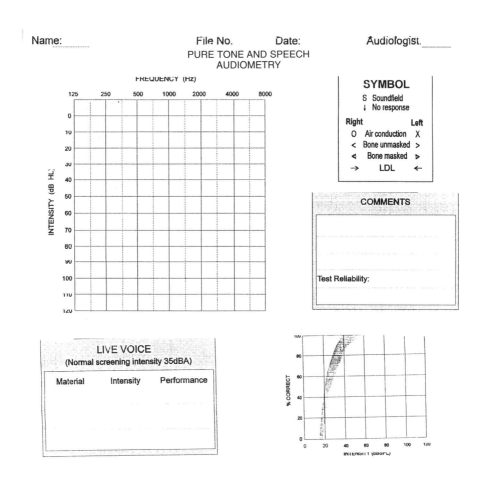

APPENDIX 3:2

Steps in the use of an immittance meter.

1. Fit headpiece. Choose appropriate sized probe tip, place on probe and insert in ear canal. To help achieve a good fit, the pinna should be gently pulled upwards and backwards to straighten the ear canal.
2. Check air-tight seal. Turn air pressure to +200mmW. If this remains static, there is a seal.
3. Turn sensitivity control to 1.
4. Move compliance knob till the balance needle points to 0.
5. Note compliance from cursor (movable indicator) on compliance scale.
6. Decrease air pressure from 200mmW watching balance meter until a maximum point is reached (so that further decrease in pressure sends the needle up again). Set air pressure at this point (middle ear pressure) and record this. (If balance needle goes off the scale bring it back with compliance knob.)
7. Move compliance knob till balance needle points to 0.
8. Read off compliance at this pressure.
9. Turn sensitivity to 0.
10. Increase air pressure to +200mmW.
11. Turn sensitivity to 1.
12. Turn compliance so that balance needle points to +5.
13. Put pen down on X-Y recorder.
14. Turn X-Y recorder on.
15. Switch on pressure varying motor.
16. Turn motor when pressure reaches -200mmW (unless MEP has not yet been shown, then continue to -4mmW).
17. Lift pen.
18. Turn X-Y recorder off.
19. Set pressure at MEP.
20. Turn sensitivity to 3.
21. Set balance meter to 0 (using compliance knob).
22. Present tones 500-4,000 Hz (first at maximum outputs to determine the presence or absence of reflexes) observing corresponding variations on the balance meter. If reflexes are present at maximum output, decrease intensity in steps to find the reflex threshold. Record thresholds for all frequencies.
23. Turn sensitivity to 0.
24. Remove probe tip and headpiece and switch off meter.

APPENDIX 5:1

INTERNATIONAL PHONETIC SYMBOLS

VOWELS   **CONSONANTS**

Short   Unvoice   Voiced

I	p_i_t	p as in path	b as in bath
e	p_e_t	t as in tap	d as in dog
æ	p_a_t	k as in kite	g as in goat
ʌ	b_u_t	wh as in when	w as in wash
o	p_o_t	f as in four	v as in van
ʊ	f_oo_t	θ as in _th_in	∂ as in _the_
ə	f_ath_er	∫ as in _sh_op	ʒ as in measure

Long

Square brackets are used to denote the use of phonetics e.g. [∂ en] for then.

i	f_ee_t
a	p_ar_t
ɔ:	p_or_t
u	b_oo_t
ə:	_per_t

Diphthongs

ei	d_ay_
ai	d_ie_
i	b_oy_
u	g_o_
au	c_ow_
ie	h_ere_
e	th_ere_
u	t_our_

APPENDIX 8:1

THE NATIONAL DEAF CHILDREN'S SOCIETY'S PROVISION

The NDCS is working for all hearing impaired children and provides:

- Advice and information on any aspect of deafness
- Information about hearing tests and hearing aids
- Information and advice on Glue Ear
- Advice on technology and equipment for your child
- The opportunity to try equipment in your own home
- Support with benefit claims and Disability Appeal Tribunals
- Advice and information on education including Further and
- Higher education
- A Teacher of the Deaf Scholarship
- Support at Special Educational Needs Tribunals
- Training courses and special events
- TALK magazine and a range of publications
- Translations of publications in Asian languages
- Grants to families with deaf children
- Social Events
- Opportunities to meet other parents and deaf children
- A Festival of Performing Arts
- Training for professionals
- Consultancy
- Child protection information and advice
  Charity Registration Number 1016532
  The Society uses the term "deaf" to cover all types of hearing loss

NDCS National Office,
15 Dufferin Street,
London EC1Y 8PD
UK

APPENDIX 8:2

The "Listening Bus" of the National Deaf Children's Society obtained with assistance from the Midland Bank travels throughout the United Kingdom publicising audiological and educational aids for hearing impaired children.

APPENDIX 8:3

HEARING AND HARNESSES - N.D.C.S.

Child Size
Suitable for children aged 2-8 years approximately. Available in red, grey or navy blue, with either a single or double pocket (depending on whether one or two hearing aids are worn). Each pocket has a Velcro strip to ensure the hearing aid stays in the pocket with the minimum amount of movement. All straps are fully adjustable.

Baby Size
Same as above, but with an additional strap that goes over the top of the hearing aid for added security, particularly when baby is crawling. Suitable for babies 6-24 months approximately.

Large Size
Same as the child harness, very adjustable and large enough to fit adults (in navy blue only).

RADIO HARNESSES & WAIST BELTS

Chest Harnesses for Children
Specially made to ensure that expensive aids sit secure and snug on a child's chest. All harnesses are adjustable and are available in red, grey or navy blue, for children from 18 months - 7 years approximately. The pockets are designed to cater for the special features of the different radio aids available.

Waist Belts for Children (up to 28" waist)
Designed to ensure the radio aid will be as secure as possible on the waist of the child.

Waist Belts for Parents/Teachers (up to 42" waist)
Larger version of the above and suitable for most transmitters as well as receivers.

NDCS, Technology Information Centre, 4 Church Road
Edgbaston, Birmingham B15 3TD, England
Telephone: 0121 454 5151 (voice/text)   Fax: 0121 454 5044

APPENDIX 11:1

THE AMERICAN JOURNAL OF OTOLOGY/ VOLUME 15, NUMBER 1 January 1994

Editorial

THE ETHICS OF COCHLEAR IMPLANTS IN YOUNG CHILDREN

Cochlear implants have become a very useful tool in the rehabilitation of profoundly hearing impaired individuals. These highly sophisticated devices are expensive, and require careful evaluation of potential candidates, delicate surgery, and, in many cases, years of user training to provide optimum benefit. The parents must bear the responsibility of making the decision for their child to undergo this procedure. Many of these parents are devastated, some feel guilty, all are anxious about the deafness of their child. The cochlear implant team has the responsibility for objectively evaluating the child, the family, and the environment to be sure that implantation is the proper means of dealing with a particular child's problem.

Whereas there have been relatively few objections to the use of implants in postlingually deaf adults, this is not the case when dealing with young children. Here the objections have been loud, repeated, and disturbing. It has been stated that cochlear implants do not work, that cochlear implant surgery is experimental and excessively risky, that cochlear implants should not have been approved by the Food and Drug Administration, and that that approval should be withdrawn. It has been said that those "audists" who are involved with implants do it for the money or out of a misguided sense of paternalism. Parents of deaf children have no right to make this decision for the child but should wait until the child is grown and old enough to decide for himself or herself, it has been argued, and parents of a deaf child have no right to *force* their child to have a cochlear implant. The parent in fact has the responsibility to make this sort of decision for the child. Only when a parental decision is deemed to be harmful to the child, as in the refusal to accept orthodox medical treatment for conditions such as cancer or to allow blood transfusion when needed on religious or philosophical grounds, may the courts step in and impose a decision over the parents' objections. Deaf children of hearing parents are not members of the deaf community until they either are placed in that community by their parents or voluntarily decide to enter it.

Cochlear implants work. There is a large body of scientific evidence, reported in the peer reviewed medical and audiological literature, that cochlear implants benefit several large segments of the hearing impaired and deaf population. This benefit is demonstrably superior to that obtained from hearing aids or vibrotactile devices. The questions as to whether or not cochlear implants really are efficacious should no longer be asked, since the evidence is too strong, so well documented and so clear. All patients should obtain an auditory sensation, become aware of sound in the environment, and be better able to modulate their voices, and to communicate by adding an auditory sensation to vision. Sixty percent of those who receive multichannel implants are able to understand at least some speech without lipreading. Even congenitally deaf children obtain a significant amount of open-set speech understanding in time after using their cochlear implants. In our series of 72 children implanted with the Nucleus device, 70 were pre-linguistically or congenitally deaf, 21 of whom were implanted at the age of 3 or younger. Of these, 16 were followed for at least 1 year and 14 had some measurable open-set discrimination. None had even closed-set understanding preoperatively. The use of cochlear implants for the young deaf child requires years of training, habilitation, and devotion by teachers, speech pathologists, and parents. The parents must be willing to spend time daily in speaking with the child, listening to the child, and helping him or her to practice both hearing and speaking. There must be a school environment where the training is oral rather than manual or, at the least, a total communication setting in which there is opportunity to learn both. A small number of congenitally and pre-linguistically deafened adults have received implants. Typically they do not receive open-set speech understanding, but their ability to communicate is enhanced. There is clearly a window of opportunity that allows the congenitally deaf child to achieve optimum results if implanted relatively early. To allow the child to make the decision as a young adult would be to preclude the maximum benefit from a cochlear implant.

Complications of cochlear implant surgery in the child have been infrequent and not life-threatening. In short, surgery is not experimental, nor is it more hazardous for the child than the adult.

There have been statements made that "audists," that is, those who are concerned with aural/oral communication for the deaf, insist on cochlear implants in children either out of a mistaken sense of paternalism and arrogance, or because it is "what they do" and a source of financial gain. Although there may be an essence of paternalism inherent in both education and health care this stems from a desire to help hearing impaired individuals to obtain an education and to live and work more comfortably in what is, after all, a predominantly hearing society.

Some advocates state that deafness is not a disability, that deafness is not a handicap, that American Sign Language (ASL) is a full equivalent to spoken English. Although it is understandable that one feels a need to defend one's way of life, deafness is legally recognised as both a handicap and a disability, and whereas ASL is a rich syntactical language, it is used by relatively few, and has no written equivalent.

Members of the cochlear implant teams seek to assist these children not for monetary gain but out of a desire to help the individual. These activities are extremely labor intensive and are often poorly reimbursed. We are clearly not in it for the money.

Is there a conspiracy to damage the deaf community? Are we attempting to eliminate deaf culture? To both questions the answer is "no". We are, however, inevitably going to diminish the numbers of young children who would otherwise enter the deaf community. Every young child who receives a cochlear implant has the potential to remain in the hearing majority of our society. Thus, over a period of years, the net effect on the deaf culture may well be a negative one. However, the child will ultimately have the ability to make the choice to wear the implant or not; to remain in the hearing majority or to cease using the implant and enter the deaf community to become a part of the deaf culture if he or she so desires. That choice will eventually be up to the child, but what we will have accomplished will be to have given the choice to that child. To defer implantation until adulthood would be to remove the choice. To implant a child at an early age is to give that child the *opportunity* to learn to hear and to speak and finally to make a decision as to which direction to follow at some time in the future. It is understandable for members of the deaf community to defend their lifestyle, which in many cases, was thrust upon them by their deafness. They have the right to make their own choice. Nevertheless, they are not entitled to speak for all young deaf children; nor should they be allowed to deprive that child of the choice, now or in the future.

Noel L. Cohen, M.D.
Department of Otolaryngology
NYU School of Medicine
New York, New York

APPENDIX 12:1

MARION DOWNS NATIONAL CENTER
FOR INFANT HEARING

The U.S. Public Health Service recently awarded a $1.2 million grant to the University of Colorado, Boulder to co-ordinate the implementation of universal newborn hearing screening programs in 17 states. These states include Alabama, Arizona, Arkansas, Colorado, Hawaii, Oklahoma, Kansas, Louisiana, Massachusetts, Minnesota, Michigan, New Mexico, Tennessee, Texas, Rhode Island, Virginia and Wyoming. The grant establishes the Marion Downs National Center for Infant Hearing, a center for the co-ordination of statewide systems for screening, diagnosis, and intervention for newborns and infants with hearing impairment. The Center is named in honor of Dr. Marion Downs, a world renowned pioneer in pediatric audiology.

Late identification of hearing loss presents a significant public health problem. 3 out of 1000 babies are born with permanent hearing loss. However, without screening, children with hearing loss are usually not identified until 2 years of age, which results in significant delays in speech, language, social, cognitive and emotional development. In contrast, early identification and intervention prior to 6 months of age has a significant positive impact on development. Researchers at the University of Colorado have recently shown that children identified at birth with mild-to-severe hearing loss and who receive intervention before 6 months fall within a normal range of language comprehension and expression as well as social development. Children with hearing loss diagnosed after six months of age experience significant delays in both language and social development.

A primary goal of the Marion Downs Center is to establish universal hearing screening (85% of births) in the 17 states by the year 2,000. Because screening for hearing loss in itself does not guarantee a positive outcome, the Center will also focus on what happens *after* screening. Families need to receive appropriate information and services following newborn screening. The center seeks to identify hearing loss by 3 months of age, to provide amplification as early as possible, to start intervention services by 6 months of age, and to measure the impact of early identification of hearing loss on development.

Colorado is uniquely prepared to undertake these goals. It has, without any major funding, put in place a universal screening program at which 60% of the state's 54,000 births are screened. Colorado also has in place an organisational structure that places 75% of all children with hearing loss in the state in appropriate intervention by six months of age, 50% by the age of three months.

The Center places a high priority on the involvement of parent and consumer groups. Advisory boards, which will be set up to help states develop plans for co-ordinated systems of screening, assessment and intervention, will include public health personnel (Maternal Child Health Directors, Directors of Speech and Hearing Programs in State and Welfare Agencies), physicians, audiologists, educators, parents and representatives of the deaf community.

Dr. Downs said the establishment of the center in her honor signifies a national commitment to improving the lives of children who are born deaf or hear of hearing. "If a child can be identified at birth and receive immediate intervention, we have done our jobs," she said. "On the other hand, if we don't detect the hearing loss until the child reaches 2-1/2, that child has, in most cases, lost the opportunity to catch up with others his or hew own age. Why, with all the tools we have, would we not spend the time to establish a model for screening and early intervention in our nation's hospitals?"

For more information on the Marion Downs National Center, contact (303) 492-6283, email at mdnc@colorado.edu or write to The University of Colorado, Department of Speech, Language and Hearing Sciences, Marion Downs National Center for Infant Hearing, Campus Box 409, Boulder, Colorado 80309-0409.

ILLUSTRATIONS

BIBLIOGRAPHY

1.	Abberton, E., Hazan, V., Fourcin, A. (1987) : Speech pattern acquisition in profoundly deaf children. In Proceedings XIth International Congress of Phonetic Sciences USSR.

2.	Archbold, S., Robinson, K. (1997) : Cochlear implantation, associated rehabilitation services and their educational implications: UK and Europe Deafness and Education (JBATOD), 21:1.

3.	Bamford, J., Davis, A., (1998) : Neonatal hearing screening; a step towards better services for children and families BJA 32, 1-6.

4.	Bang, C. (1980) : A world of sound and music: music therapy and musical speech therapy with hearing impaired children. Brit. Association of Teachers of the Deaf (BATOD).

5.	Barr, B. (1963:2) : Psychogenic deafness in school children. Int. Audiol.

6.	Bartkin, B. (1988) : Reducing the stigma of deafness - hearing aids with enhance visual appeal. Br J Audiol, 167-9, August 22(3).

7.	BATOD, (1985) : Implant Centre teachers of the deaf: Code of Practice JBATOD, 19/5, 135-141.

8.	Beagley, H.A., (Editor) (1981) : Audiology and audiological medicine, Oxford.

9.	Bench, J. and Bamford, J. (1978) : Speech and hearing tests, Academic Press.

10.	Békèsy, G. (1947) : The recruitment phenomenon and difference limen in hearing and vibration sense, Laryngoscope, 57:765-77.

11.	Bergon, D.B. (1983) : Ear disease in a group general practice. J. Laryngol Otol, 97(9):817-24.

12.	Bess, F.H. (Ed) (1983) : Hearing impairment in children, York Press Inc. Maryland 21120 (1988) 97 (9):817-24.

13. Black. R.C., Clark, G.M., Patrick, J.F. (October 1981) : Current distribution measurements within the human cochlear, IEE Trans Biomed Eng, 28(10):721-5.

14. Bones, C., Diggory, S. (1999) : An evaluation of one cochlear implant user's speech perception : with and without an FM system and lip pattern in controlled background noise levels. Deafness and Education International 1(2), 83-95.

15. Boothroyd, A. (1978) : Detection of temporal gaps by deaf and normal subjects, SARP, No.12, Clarke School for Deaf Children, Northampton, Mass.

16. Bredberg, G. (1988) : Results from extracochlear 3M/Vienna implants on 10 patients, Acta O. Suppl Stockh., 449:59-62.

17. British Society of Audiology (1988) : Description for pure tone audiograms, BJA, 22:123.

18. British Standards Institution (1954) : the normal threshold of hearing for pure tones by earphone listening, London, The Institution, BS2497.

19. Brooks, D.N. (1971) : A new approach to identification audiometry, Audiology, 10:334-9.

20. Brooks, D.N., Geohegan, P.M. (1992) : Non-organic hearing loss in young persons.

21. Busby, P.A., Tong, Y.C., Clark, G.M. (February 1993) : Electrode position, repetition rate and speech perception by early and late-deafened cochlear implant patients, J Acoust Soc Am., 93(2):1058-67.

22. Busby, P.A., Tong, Y.C., Clark, G.M. (1993) : The perception of temporal modulations by cochlear implant patients, JASA, 94 (1):124-31.

23. Carhart, R. (1946) : Monitored live-voice as a test of auditory acuity, JASA, 17339-49.

24. Carhart, R. (1951) : Basic principles of speech audiometry, Acta O. Stockh., 40:62-71.

25. Carhart. R. (1957) : clinical determination of abnormal auditory adaptation, Arch Otolaryng, Chicago, 65:32-9.

26.   Carhart, R. (1958) : The usefulness of the binaural hearing aid, <u>JSHRK</u>, 23:42-51.

27.   Carhart, R., Jerger, J.F. (1959) : Preferred method for clinical determination of pure-tone thresholds, <u>JSHD</u>, 24:330-345.

28.   Cawthorne, T., Harvey, R.M. (1953) : A comparison between hearing for pure tones and for speech, <u>J. Laryng</u>, 67:233-47.

29.   Chaiklin, J.B., Ventry, I.M. (1963) : Functional hearing loss. In: Jerger, Editor. Modern Developments in Audiology, New York: Academic Press, 76-125.

30.   Clark, G.M., Tong, Y.C. (1982) : A multiple channel cochlear implant - a survey of results with two patients, <u>Arch. Otolaryng</u>, 214-7.

31.   Cohen, N.L. (January 1994) : The ethics of cochlear implants in young children, <u>Amer J Otology</u>, 15(1) (Editorial).

32.   Cole, W.A. (1987) : Present and future developments in hearing aid design, <u>J Otolaryngology</u>, 8(10:1-9).

33.   Dale, D.M.C. (1968 and 1971) : <u>Deaf Children at home and at school</u>, Lonodn University Press and Charles C. Thomas Ltd., Springfield, Illinois.

34.   Dale, D.M.C. (1978) : Educating deaf and partially hearing children individually in ordinary schools, The Lancet, 8095(11):884-887.

35.   Dale, D.M.C. (1984) : <u>Individualised integration: studies of deaf and partially hearing children in ordinary schools and colleges</u>, London, Hodder and Stoughton Ltd., and Charles C. Thomas Ltd., Springfield, Illinois.

36.   Dale, D.M.C. (1958) : the possibility of providing extensive auditory experience for severely and profoundly deaf children by means of hearing aids (<u>Ph.D. thesis</u>), Manchester University.

37.   Dale, D.M.C. (1987) : The psychological investigation of intellectual development in deaf children, <u>M.Sc. dissertation</u>, University of Cambridge.

38.   David, H., Kranz, F. (1964) : International audiometric zero, <u>JASA</u>, 36:1450-4.

39.   Davis, H., Stevens, S.S., Nichols, R.H., Hudgins, C.V., Peterson, G.E., Marquis, R.J., et al. (1947) : <u>Hearing aids: an experimental study of design objectives</u>, Cambridge: Harvard University Press.

40.   Delk, J.H. (1983) : <u>Comprehensive Dictionary of Audiology</u>, Harvard, Mass, Laux.

41.   Denes, P. Nauton, R.F. (1950) : The clinical detection of auditory recruitment, <u>J Laryng</u>, 64:375-378.

42.   Derbyshire, A.J., Farley, J.C. (1959) : Sampling auditory responses at the cortical level, <u>Ann. Otol</u>, 68:675-697.

43.   Dix, M.R., Hallpike, C.S., Hood, J.D. (1948) : Observations upon the loudness recruitment phenomenon with especial reference to the differential diagnosis of disorders of the internal ear and VIIIth nerve, <u>J Laryng</u>, 62:671-86.

44.   Dryden, R.A. : Study of the collaboration between implant professionals and local educators in the rehabilitation of children with cochlear implants, <u>JBATOD Deafness in Education</u>, 21/2.

45.   Egan, J.P. (1948) : Articulation testing methods, <u>Laryngoscope</u>, 58:955-91.

46.   Eilers, R.E., Vergara, K., Oller, D.K., Balkany, T.J. (1992) : Evaluating hearing impaired children's usage of tactual vocoders, <u>Proceedings of the second international conference on tactual aids, hearing aids and cochlear implants</u>, Stockholm, Sweden: Dept. of Speech.

47.   Erber, N.P. (1979) : "speech perception by profoundly hearing-impaired children", <u>JHSD</u>, 44(3):225-270.

48.   Ewing, A.W.G. (1956) ; History of the department of education of the deaf, University of Manchester, 1919-1955, <u>Br Journ Educ Studies</u>, 4:103-28.

49.   Ewing, A.W.G. (Editor) (1960) : <u>The modern educational treatment of deafness</u>, Manchester University Press.

50.   Ewing, A.W.G., Ewing, E.C. (1964) : <u>Teaching deaf children to talk</u>, Manchester University Press.

51.   Ewing, A.W.G., Littler, T.S. (1935) : Auditory fatigue and adaptation, <u>Br J Psychol</u>, 25:284-307.

52. Ewing, A.W.G., Ewing, I.R. (1944) : The ascertainment of deafness in infancy and early childhood, J Laryng, 59:303-33.

53. Ewing, A.W.G., Ewing, I.R. (1954) : Speech and the deaf child, University of Manchester Press.

54. Fant, G. (1948) : Analys av de svenska konsonantjuden, Stockholm, LME Report, No. 1064.

55. Fearn, R.W. (1976) : Calibration of audiometers, J Sound Vibration, 46:151.

56. Fifield, D.B., Earnshaw, R., Smither, M. 91980) : A new ear impression technique to prevent acoustic feedback with high powered hearing aids, Volta Review, 82:33-9.

57. Fletcher, H. (1953) : Speech and hearing in communication, New York: Van Nostrand.

58. Fletcher, H., Steinberg, J.C. (1930) : Articulation testing methods, J Acoust Soc Amer, 2 Pts:1-97.

59. Fowler, E.P. (1950) : Recruitment of loudness phenomenon, Laryngoscope, 60:680-95.

60. Freeland, A. (1989) : Deafness: the facts, Oxford University Press.

61. French, N.R., Steinberg, J.C. (1947) : Factors governing the intelligibility of speech sounds, J Acoust Soc Amer, 19:90-119.

62. Fry, D.B., Kerridge, P.M.J. (1939) : Tests for the hearing of speech by deaf children, The Lancet, 1:106-9.

63. Gulick, W., Gescheider, G.A., Frisina, R.D. (1989) : Hearing -

Physiological acoustics, neural coding and psychoacoustics, Oxford University Press.

64. Haggard, M. (1992) : Screening tests of hearing, BJA, 26:209-215.

65. Haig, L. (1980) : The standardisation of three tests of vowel discrimination, (M.Sc) London: Bartholemews Hospital, University of London.

66.   Harbert, F., Stataloff, J.A. (1955) : Clinical application of recruitment and masking, Laryngoscope, 65:113-23.

67.   Hardy, W.G., Bordley, J.R. (1951) : Special techniques in testing the hearing of children, PGSR audiometry, J Speech Hearing Dis, 16:125-31.

68.   Harold, B.B. (1957) : The effect of variations in intensity on the capacity of deaf children and adults to hear speech with hearing aids. (Ph.D. thesis), Manchester University.

69.   Hawkins, D., Naidoo, S. (1933) : Comparison of sound quality and clarity with asymmetrical peak clipping and output limiting compression, J Amer Acad of Audiol, 4(4).

70.   Hazell, J.W.P. (1984) : Spontaneous cochlear acoustic emissions and tinnitus: Clinical experience in the tinnitus patient, J Laryng and Otol, 9:106-10.

71.   Hazell, J.W.P. (December 7 1995) : Support for a neurophysiological model of tinnitus: Research data and clinical experience, Proc Vth International Tinnitus Seminar, Portland, Oregon, 579-82.

72.   Hazell, J.W.P. (February 1990) : The practical management of sensorineural tinnitus, J Otolaryng, 19(1):1-8.

73.   Hirsch, I.J. (1952) : The measurement of hearing, New York: McGraw.

74.   Hirsch, I.J., Palva, T., Goodman, A. (1954) : Difference limen and recruitment, Arch Otolaryng, 60:525-40.

75.   Hodges, A.V., Ruth, R.A., Lambert, P.R., Balkany, T.J. (October 1994) : Electric auditory brainstem responses in nucleus multichannel cochlear implant users, Arch Otolaryng Head Neck Surg, 120(10):1993-9.

76.   Hood, J.D. (1950) : Studies in auditory fatigue and adaptation, Acta Otolaryng, Stockholm, (Suppl 92).

77.   Hudgins, C.V. (1953) : Response of profoundly deaf children to auditory training, J Speech Hearing Dis, 18:273-88.

78.   Hudgins, C.V. (1958) : Personal communication.

79. Hudgins, C.V., Marquis, R.J., Nichols, R.H., Peterson, G.E., Ross, D.A. (1948) : The comparative performance of an experimental hearing aid and two commercial instruments, JASA, 20:241-58.

80. Hughson, W., Westlake, H. : Manual for programme outline for rehabilitation of aural casualties both military and civil, Trans Amer Acad Ophthal Otolaryng, Sup. 48:1-15.

81. Huizing, H. (1951) : Auditory training, Acta O, Stockholm Suppl., 100:158-63.

82. Irwin, R.J., Stillman, J.A., Schade, A. (1986) ; The width of the auditory filter in children, J Exp Child Psych, 41:429-442.

83. Irwin, R.J., Ball, A.K., Stillman, J.A., Rosser, J. (1986) : The development of auditory acuity in children, Child Dev, 56:614-637.

84. Jastreboff, P.J. (1990) : Phantom auditory perception (tinnitus): mechanisms of generation and perception, Neurosci Res, 8:221-254.

85. Jaussi, K.R. (1994) : Hearing: a second language for children with cochlear implants, Perspectives in education and deafness, 13(2):17-19, Care Project (Classroom for Auditory Enriched Education) developed by educators at the University of Arkansas and the Arkansas children's hospital for children with cochlear implants.

86. Jerger, J.F. (1952) ; A difference limen test and its diagnostic significance, Laryngoscope, 62:1316-32.

87. Jerger, J.F. (1975) : Diagnostic uses of impedance measures, Handbook of clinical impedance audiometry, New York: Dobbs Ferry/Morgan Press.

88. Jerger, J.F., Stach, B.A. (1987) : Immittance measures in auditory disorders, In: Jacobsen, J.T., Northern, J.L., Diagnostic audiology, Austin, Tex.: Pro-Ed.

89. John, J.E.J., Howarth, J.N. (1965) : The effect of time distortions on the intelligibility of deaf children's speech, Language and speech, 8:127-34.

90. John, J.E.J., Thomas, H. (1957) : Design and construction of schools for the deaf. In: Ewing, A.W.G., Editor, Educational guidance and the deaf child, Manchester, Manchester University Press, 176-87.

91.   Katz, J. (Editor), (1985) : Handbook of clinical audiology, Baltimore: Williams and Williams.

92.   Kemp, D.T., (1978) : Stimulated acoustic emissions from within the human auditory system, <u>JASA</u>, 64:1386-91.

93.   Kemp, D.T., (1980) : Towards a model for the origin of cochlear echoes, <u>Hearing research</u>, 80.

94.   Kendall, D.C., (1953) : The mental development of young deaf children, (<u>Ph.D. Thesis</u>), Manchester University.

95.   Kileny, P.R., Zwolan, T.A., Zimmerman-Phillips, S., Telian, S.A. (October, 1994) : Electrically evoked auditory brainstem response in pediatric patients with cochlear implants, <u>Arch Otolaryng Head Neck Surg.</u>, 120(10):1083-90.

96.   Lass, N.J., Tecca, J.E., Woodford, C.M. (1987) : Teachers' knowledge of, exposure to and attitudes toward hearing aids and hearing aid wearers, <u>Language speech and hearing services in schools</u>, 18:86-95.

97.   Liden, G. (1954) : Speech audiometry - an experimental and clinical study with Swedish language material, <u>Acta O</u>, Suppl. 114.

98.   Ling, D. (1979) : <u>Speech and the hearing impaired child</u>: theory and practice, Washington, D.C., Alexander Graham Bell Association for the Deaf.

99.   Lurie, M.H. (1940) : Studies of acquired and inherited deafness in animals, <u>JASA</u>, 11:420-426.

100.   McCormick, B. (Editor), (1996) : <u>Paediatric audiology</u>, Cambridge University Press.

101.   McKay, C.M., McDermott, H.J., Clark, G.M. (November 1994) : Pitch percepts associated with amplitude-modulated current pulse trains in cochlear implantees, <u>J Acoust Soc Am</u>, 96 (5 Pt 1):2664-73).

102   Medical Research Council (1947) : <u>Hearing aids and audiometers</u>, Special Resport Series No. 261, London HMSO.

103.   Miyamoto, R.T., Robbins, A.M., Osberger, M.J., Todd, S.L., Riley, A.I., Kirk, K. (1995) : Comparison of multichannel tactile aids and cochlear

implants in children with profound hearing impairments, <u>AJLO</u>, 16(1):8-13.

104.   Moore, B.C.J., Glasberg, R.F., Stone, M.A. (1999) : Signal processing to compensate for reduced dynamic range, <u>BJA</u>, 33,124-258.

105.   Murray, N. Tye, Spencer, L., Bedia, E., Gilbert, (1995) : Relationships between speech production and speech perception skills in young cochlear implant users, <u>AORL</u>, 98(5):2454-2460.

106.   Murray, N.Tye, Spencer, L., Woodworth, G. (1995) ; Acquisition of speech by children who have prolonged cochlear implant experience, <u>JSHR</u>, 38(2):327-337.

107.   National Institute of Health, Office of the Director, (1994) : Early identification of hearing impairment in infants and young children, <u>Amer J Otol</u>, 15:4.

108.   National Institute of Health, (1995) : Cochlear implants in adults and children, NIN Consensus Statement, 13(2):1-30.

109.   Nilsson, G. (1942) ; Some aspects of the differential diagnosis of obstructive and neural deafness, <u>Acta Otolaryng</u>, 30:125-138.

110.   Northern, J.L., Downs, M.P. (1974) : <u>Hearing in children</u>, Baltimore: Williams and Wilkins, 1974.

111.   Northern, J.L. (1989) : <u>Diagnostic audiology</u>, Austin, Texas Pro-Ed Publishing.

112.   Numbers, M.E., Hudgins, C.V. : Speech perception in present day education of deaf children, <u>Volta Review</u>, 50:449-456.

113.   Osberger, M.J., Maso, M., Leslie, K.S. (1993) : speech intelligibility of children with cochlear implants, tactile aids or hearing aids, <u>JSHR</u>, 36:186-203.

114.   Palva, T. (1952) : Finnish speech audiometry, Acta O, Suppl. 101.

115   Pascoe, D.P. (1986) : <u>Hearing aids. Pro-ed studies in communication disorders</u>, Austin, Texas.

116   Patrick, J.F., Clark, G.M. (August 1991) : The Nucleus 22-channel cochlear implant system, <u>Ear Hear</u>, 12(4 Suppl):3S-9S.

117   Penner, M. (1992) : Linking spontaneous otoacoustic emissions and tinnitus, Br J Audiol, 26:115-23.

118   Pollack, M.C. and Morgan, R. (128-129)

119.   Probst, R., Lonsbury-Martin, B.L., Martin, G.K., Coats, A.C. (1987) : Otoacoustic emissions in ears with hearing loss, Am J Otolaryng, 8(2):73-81, Mar-Apr.

120.   Purdy, S.C., Chard, L.L., Moran, C.A., Hodgson, S.A. (1995) : Outcomes of cochlear implants for new Zealand children and their families, AORL, Suppl 166:102-105.

121.   Rebillard, G., Abbour, S., Lenoir, M. (1987) : Les oto-emissions acoustiques.11. Les oto-emissions spontanees: resultats chez des sujets normaux ou presentat des acouphenes, Ann Otolaryngol Chir Cervicofac, 104(5):363-8.

122.   Robson, J. (1979) : (Screening techniques in babies, Sound, 4(4):91-4.

123.   Roeser, R.J., Roland, P. (1992) : What audiologists must know about cerumen and cerumen management, Amer J Audiol, 1(4):27-35.

124.   Ronnei, E.C. (1951) : Learning to look and listen, Teachers' college, Columbia University.

125.   Ross, M. (1991): A future challenge: educating the educators and public about hearing loss, Seminars in hearing, 12(4):402-11.

126.   Ross, M. (1972) : Classroom acoustics and speech intelligibility. In: Katz, J., Editor, Handbook of Clinical Audiology, Baltimore: Williams & Wilkins.

127.   Ross, M. (Editor) (1991) : Hearing impaired children in the mainstream, Parkton, M.D.: York Press.

128.   Ross, M., Madell, J. (1988) : The premature demise of body-worn hearing aids, ASHA, 30(11):29.

129.   Ross, M. Seewald, R. (1988) : Hearing aid selection and evaluation with young children, In: Bess,F., Editor, Hearing impairment in children, York Press.

215

130. Sarant, J.Z., Cowan, R.S.C., Blamey, P.J., Galvin, K.L., Clark, G.M. (1994) : Cochlear implants for congenitally deaf adolescents: is open-set speech perception a realistic expectation? Ear and Hearing, 15(5):400-403.

131. Sheldrake, J.B., Jastreboff, P.J., Hazell, J.W.P. (December 7, 1995) : Perspectives for the total elimination of tinnitus perception, Proc, Vth International Tinnitus Seminar, Portland, Oregon, p. 531-537.

132. Simmons, A. Alexander Graham Bell Arch. (1996) : Otolaryng. 84 24-76.

133. Smith, K. Hodgson, W. (1997) : The effects of systematic reinforcement on the speech discrimination responses of normal and hearing impaired children, J. Aud, Res. 10:110-117.

134. Spencer, L.M., (1970) : The construction of a test of the Intelligibility of Speech of Hearing. Impaired Children. Ph.D. Thesis University of London Institute of Education.

135. Stach, B.A., Jerger, J.F. (1989) : Immittance measures in auditory disorders. In: Jacobsen, J.T., Northern, J.R., Diagnostic Audiology, Austin, Texas: Pro-Ed Publishing, Chapter 6.

136. Stelmachowicz, P.G., Mace, A.L., Kopun, J.G., Carney, E. (June 1993) : Long and short term characteristics of speech: implications for hearing aid selection for young children, J Speech Hear Res., 36(3):609-20.

137. Subtelny, J. (1979) : Personal communication from Dr. Subtelny.

138. Taag, F. (1995) : Your child is hearing impaired. What does it mean? Communicate, 5(3), P.O. Box 34-355, Birkenhead, Auckland, NZ.

139. Tait, M., Lutman, M.E. (1994) : Comparison of early communicative behavior in young children with cochlear implants and with hearing aids, Ear and Hearing, 15(5):352-381.

140. Tong, Y.C., Clark, G.M., Blamey, P.J., Busby, P.A., Dowell, R.C. (1982) : Psychophysical studies of two multiple channel cochlear implant patients, JASA, 71(1):153-60.

154. Wilson, J.P., Sutton, G.J. (1981) : Acoustic correlates of tonal tinnitus. In: Everend, D., Lawrenson, G.J., Editors, Tinnitus, London: Pitman, 81-107.

155. Yater, V.V. (1977) : <u>Mainstreaming of children with a hearing loss: practical guidelines and implications</u>, Springfield, Illinois: Charles C. Thomas.

156. Zwicker, E. (1987) : Objective otoacoustic emissions and their correlation to tinnitus, In: Feldman, H., Editor, <u>Third International Tinnitus Seminar</u>, Karlsruhe: Harsch-Verlag, 75-81.

157. Zwicker, E., Schloth, E. (1984) : Interrelation of different otoacoustic emissions, <u>JASA</u>.

158. Zwislocki, J. (1953) : Acoustic attenuation between the ears, <u>JASA</u>, 25:732-59.

INDEX

Huizing, H., 104

I

Immitance instrument, 57
    use of, 208-209
Impacted wax (Cerumen), 76, 83
Impedance, 56
    diagram, 57
    meter, 56-57
Implant, cochlear, 148-150
Improvised toy test, 50-51
India, 12
Individualised mainstream, 20, 21, 174-182
Induction loop system, 26-29
Infant screening tests, 160-163
Instituut voor Doven, 141
Internat. Standards Org.(ISO), 9
Internat. Phonetic Symbols, 192
Intelligible speech, 202-205
Intensity, 85-86, 92
Italy, 154
ITO, 152

J

Jastreboff, P.J., 119
Jerger, 8, 56, 66
Jerger, J.F., Hayes, D., 72
John JEJ, 96
John J.E.J. and Howarth, J.N., 123, 136
John, J.E.J. and Thomas, H., 94
John Tracey Clinic, 145
Joshua, 155

K

Karchmer, 136
Keith, 13, 63

Kendall, 40
Kerridge and Fry, 39
Killion, 130
K/T/ tests, 44, 45, 185
Kyeton and Balkany, 153

L

Lack of voice control, 71
Larynx, 78
Latham and Haggard, 165
Leslie, 152
Liden, G., 37, 56, 102
Ling, D., 88, 131-132
Listening levels settings, 105, 108-111
Listening-reading-speaking method (LRS), 136-138
Lorente de No, 110
Loudness balance, 112
Loudness recruitment, 112
Low birth weight, 160

M

Mainstreaming (integration), 133, 155
Malingering, 70
Marion Downs Centre, 145
Masking, 36-38
Maso, 152
McCormick, 128, 154, 158, 159, 162
Ménières, 117, 118
Meningitis, 151
Menuhin, 19
Metz, 56, 61
Middle, C., 2, 140, 141
Miyamoto et al, 156
M/J word lists, 40, 43, 92, 184
Moore, 8

Morgan, R., 136
Mothers of deaf children, 13, 164
Music, 138-143

N

Naidoo, 8
National Acous. Labs., Aust., 40, 126-128
National Inst. Deafness, USA, 170
National Deaf Children's Society, 145, 192, 193
New Zealand, 152, 164-165
Nilson, 110
NOHL, 62, 64-66
Noise, 165
    excluding enclosures, 170
    speech reception and, 98
Nolan, 125
Nonsense syllables, 39
Northern, 63, 125
Northern and Downs, 125, 127
Norway, 154
Nucleus mini systems, 150
Nucleus 22 channel implant, 150-152
Numbers, Hudgins, 44, 146

O

Ohm, G.S., 64
Organ music, 141-143
Osberger, M.J. et al, 152
Orchestra, 145
Otitis media, 170
Otoacoustic emissions (OAE) tests, 163
Otosclerosis, 59, 68
Output of hearing aids, 5, 7
Overload, 4

P

Paired vowel text, 51, 52
Palva, T., 39, 67
Parents, 27, 39, 55, 89, 128, 133-134, 136, 137
Pascall, B., 26
Peak clipping, 8
Personal paging systems (PPS), 134-135
Phonak Ltd. video tapes, 167
Phonetic symbols, 210-211
Pitch, 2
Pohlman and Krantz, 112
Pollack M.C. and Morgan, R., 128-129
Preschool children, 110-111
Profoundly deaf, 72, 74-75
Psychologists, 31
Pure tone tests, 32-38

R

Rapport, 33
Rarefaction, 1
Rate of utterance, 88
Rebillard, G., 116
Receiver, 3
Reed's RNID test, 27, 183
Reference levels, 8-9
Response curves, 6
Reverberation, 93-98
Rh Incompatibility (Esp, Kernicterus), 160
Robson, J., 166
Rochester Institute of Technology, 218, 145
Ross, M., 168, 176
Royal National Institute for Deaf (RNID), 40, 41, 146
RNID Library, 146

V

Van Uden, A.M.J., 73, 136, 139, 141
Venting of earmoulds, 126-127
Vertigo, 116
Vibration, 2
Videotape recordings, 142
Visiting teachers, 137
Vocal cords (folds), 77
Volta, A., 146
Volta Bureau, 145
Volta Review, 146
Von Békèsy, 66, 114, 115, 124, 126
Vowel discrimination tests, 45-52
Vowel production, 77, 84-86
Volume control settings, 105
Volume ear canals, Fig. 7:8, 111
Vowel production tests, 190

W

Waist belts for parents/teachers, 194
Watson, T.J., 40
Wax (cerumen), 68, 83
Wedenberg, E., 87
Whitestone, H., 11
White noise, 37
Word lists, 183-190

Y

Yale University, 150
Yater, V.V., 133

Z

Zwicker and Schloth, 116
Zwicker, E., 116
Zwiczlocki, J., 37